INTRODUCTION

The county of Cumbria which was formed in 1971 with the modifying of the old county boundary system, brought together some of the finest natural habitat in the country. Although it has taken a long time for the local people to get used to this amalgamation, to describe the natural beauty of the whole of this large county, would be even more difficult.

We are indeed very fortunate in having every possible type of habitat found elsewhere in Britain located in one county and with it a range of wildlife and flora which is very rich and varied.

The birdlife of the county is also very rich and although the older generation of ornithologist will refer to the loss of birds like the Corncrake, Nightjar and Black Grouse from many areas, we have seen in recent years the introduction or expansion of birds like Peregrine, Collared Dove and Siskin to the county.

Apart from the many various bird habitats we are fortunate with the location of Cumbria, as we have several 'northern' birds breeding here on their southern limit, namely Eider, Goosander and Twite as well as 'southern' birds like Lesser Spotted Woodpecker, Reed Warbler and Lesser Whitethroat and more recently the Nuthatch reaching Cumbria.

The county also has several rare species like Golden Eagle, Black-tailed Godwit and Dotterel breeding with various degrees of success. Pressures from development of our wild places for agriculture, forestry and the various modern recreational pursuits are a constant problem for conservationists of the region, whose main aim is to see that rare species and others which have a foothold in the county can get established without undue disturbance.

Since the late Ralph Stokoe produced his 'Birds of the Lake Counties' in 1964, ornithology in its many spheres has become one of the most popular outdoor pursuits. With the increase in interest, the birdwatcher needs information to help him to understand the status of the various species he is seeing in the county. Most references can be found in the annual 'Cumbria Bird Report'. As editor of the annual natural history report, 'Birds in Cumbria' as well as the County Bird Report, I have often been asked if there was to be an updated systematic list of the county's birdlife. Many new species have been added in recent years as well as the rise and fall in the breeding population.

It was with this in mind that I set about trying to compile a check-list of species in 1979, but soon ran into difficulties as I found there was no written annual record of birds in the county between 1964 and 1970 with the failure of 'The Field Naturalist'.

It was in 1970 that the Association of Natural History Societies in Cumbria was formed, with one of their main aims being to produce a county bird report.

To fill the gap, I have contacted many of the well known ornithologists throughout the county for records as well as the various Natural History Societies, Town Museums and Libraries.

Verifying certain unusual records has been difficult as most of them have not been submitted to the British Birds Rarities Committee for their consideration. I feel it is imperative to have a record of a rarity accepted by this body before it is published on a county list. Even so I have added one or two rarities recorded in the 1960's and not submitted to the BBRC, as they have excellent descriptions. Further data of these sightings is nearly always impossible to obtain as in many cases the recorder is now deceased. I have also added some previously published but unconfirmed records underlined along with records of doubtful origin, *ie* possible feral or birds of recent captivity.

I have added an Appendix with charts of Wildfowl counts over the ten year period and an up to date list of 1985 records. Finally, for those of you who wish to use the book as a reference on a regular basis, I have put in a personal check-list of all the birds recorded in the county to date.

Acknowledgements

I would like to say thank you to everyone who has helped me in any way to compile the data produced here. In particular to Joy Ketchin and the Cumbria Trust for Nature Conservation for the use of their records as well as those of the late Ralph Stokoe, to Kathleen Atkinson and the Freshwater Biological Association for the use of their Wildfowl tables and to Shaun Lawson for his art-work.

My special thanks are due to Ian Kinley for his guiding comments and proof reading with some adjusting in some instances and to Tim Dean for helpful advice and comments and the use of Walney Bird Observatory records, and of course I must not forget Arnold Gould, without whose skill in the art of bird photography this publication would be incomplete.

COUNTY OF CUMBRIA

THE FAUNAL AREA

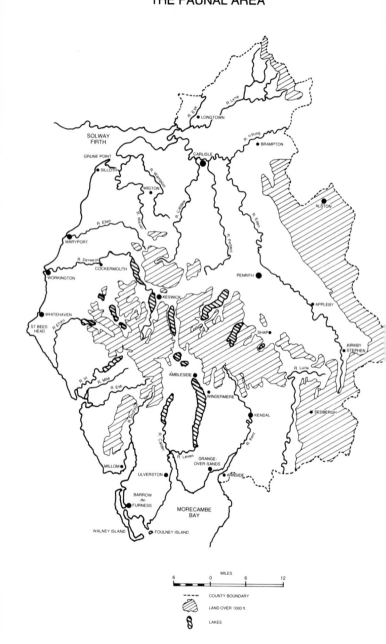

SOLWAY FIRTH

GRUNE POINT

SILLOTH

MARYPORT

WORKINGTON

WHITEHAVEN

ST BEES HEAD

MILLOM

BARROW -IN- FURNESS

WALNEY ISLAND

FOULNEY ISLAND

MORECAMBE BAY

ULVERSTON

GRANGE-OVER-SANDS

ARNSIDE

KENDAL

WINDERMERE

AMBLESIDE

KESWICK

COCKERMOUTH

WIGTON

CARLISLE

LONGTOWN

BRAMPTON

ALSTON

PENRITH

APPLEBY

SHAP

KIRKBY STEPHEN

SEDBERGH

R. Esk
R. Lyne
R. Irthing
R. Wampool
R. Waver
R. Caldew
R. Petteril
R. Eden
R. Ellen
R. Derwent
R. Ehen
R. Irt
R. Mite
R. Esk
R. Duddon
R. Crake
R. Leven
R. Kent
R. Lune

MILES

6   0   6   12

- - - - -   COUNTY BOUNDARY

LAND OVER 1000 ft.

LAKES

THE COUNTY OF CUMBRIA

This large new county, which is an amalgamate of the old counties of Cumberland, Westmorland, the Furness region of Lancashire and a small western corner of North Yorkshire contains many different areas of outstanding natural beauty. It also has more varied habitats in one region than any other county in England, ranging from its vast estuaries, its sea cliffs and sand-dunes, its woodlands and forest, its rivers, lakes and tarns to its wide open spaces on its mosses, moorland and mountain top, all of which should be considered in more detail.

Coastline
The Cumbrian coastline is not generally associated with natural beauty but never-the-less has ever changing features which are attractive to the eye.

It is so varied that it is not too hard to find quiet areas of shoreline even in the height of the summer season. Most holidaymakers generally keep to the beaches, caravan and camp-sites with easy access to towns like Silloth, Maryport and Millom.

The central part of the coastline around the towns of Workington and Whitehaven with its mining and heavy industry, is under constant pressure from pollution. The near-by reserve of St Bees Head where several thousand Auks and Gulls nest on the ledges of impressive sandstone cliffs are under particular threat. Although the various industries in the area have reduced the amount of effluent pumped into the sea there is always a threat to seabirds especially in the Spring when around 6,000 Auks gather on the sea prior to coming in to the ledges to breed.

On the Solway Firth, between the towns of Silloth and Workington, the coastline is not very varied with the agricultural land coming right down to the shore and the shore itself being mostly of shingle. There is little in the way of feeding for wading birds except around the Flimby and Siddick area of Workington where Dunlin, Knot, Bar-tailed Godwit and the elusive Purple Sandpiper can be found in small numbers in the winter. Golden Plover sites can also be found here and between Mawbray and Beckfoot further north. Sea-duck, like Scaup and Common Scoter, are found in parties around Silloth.

The summer months bring Little Terns to breed to this part of the coast but invariably they are unsuccessful due to human disturbance. During the migration periods of Spring and Autumn, passage birds increase the volume of birds to be found in this area, sometimes bringing rarer species into the locality, an example of this being the first British record of an Isabelline Wheatear found near Allonby in the autumn of 1887.

South of the red cliffs of St Bees the coastline changes again, this time to one of sand dune systems and sandy beaches. Where the estuaries of the Rivers Irt, Mite and Esk meet at Drigg and around Kirksanton and Sandscale on the Duddon estuary further south there are particularly noteworthy dune-systems. It is on the Drigg dunes that one of the largest Black-headed Gull colonies in the country flourishes as well as being an important site for several species of Tern. Between Drigg and Kirksanton the coastline is rather unproductive for birds. The only area of interest is around Selker Bay where the local coastguard station is a good sea-watching point. It is here in Summer that small rafts of moulting Red-breasted Mergansers can be found.

Walney Island deserves special mention as its strategic position on the corner of the Cumbrian coastline acts as a funnel to migrating land and sea-birds over its peninsula or around its shore according to the weather conditions. It was realised that this was an important migration site and so the Walney Bird Observatory was formed in 1964 to monitor seasonal bird movements. Walney also is the home during the breeding season for around 20,000 Herring and Lesser Black-backed Gulls, the largest gull colony in Europe. Eider also breed here, this being the furthest south that they breed on the west coast of Britain.

From Walney the coastline turns eastwards into Morecambe Bay where at low tide its vast expanses of shining silver mud flats are exposed. Here thousands of waders feed during migration and in the winter. From the gravel spit of Foulney Island to Grange-over-Sands and Arnside, large flocks of Knot, Dunlin, Oystercatcher, Curlew and Bar-tailed Godwit can be found, particularly around the Cartmel Peninsula. This area is also important for wintering wildfowl, in particular Wigeon, Teal, Pintail, Shelduck and Grey-lag Geese.

Rivers and Estuaries

Britain's prevailing moist westerly airstream and the peaks of the Lake District mountains with their high rainfall are the source of many small becks and streams which along their course merge to form Cumbria's fourteen major river systems. The two longest rivers, namely the Eden and the Lune originate in the same area of the Pennine foothills, the Eden travelling north-east through the rich Eden Valley to the Solway, the Lune running south-west through the Howgill Fells to Kirkby Lonsdale where it flows into Lancashire and on to Morecambe Bay south of Lancaster. The River Eden on its northward journey is one of the most important rivers ornithologically, especially between Appleby and Carlisle where it is at its widest and deepest in some areas. Here wildfowl have an important habitat in the winter months when Grey-lag Geese and Whooper Swans gather in good numbers. Within the city boundaries of Carlisle, the Eden is joined by the River Petteril. It is here that Kingfisher are noted regularly and Green Sandpiper can be found during the winter.

The Upper Solway estuarine marshes formed by the rivers Eden and Esk are one of Cumbria's richest bird habitats. It is an important area for nesting waders, gulls and terns and in the winter months holds a good population of wildfowl including Pink-footed and Barnacle Geese. Rockcliffe Marsh is a CTNC reserve and is naturally rigorously controlled by them, access is strictly by permit.

Further south down the Solway is Moricambe Bay, where the rivers Wampool and Weaver join the estuary. This again is another good site for waders and wildfowl during the winter months and in the migration periods. At the southern end of the Bay lies the gravel peninsula of Grune Point. This can be a particularly rewarding site during the Spring and Autumn when large numbers of migrating passerines are recorded, often with a sprinkling of rarities. It is also a good sea-watching area and holds several species of wader in winter and terns in summer.

The River Derwent originates from Derwentwater's overspill and passes through Bassenthwaite Lake to reach the sea at Workington. Although it is not very well known for its birdlife it is a good river for diving duck in winter, particularly Goldeneye and Goosander.

The River Irt also originates from a lake, this time Wastwater, and joins in an estuarine confluence at

Ravenglass with the Rivers Esk and Mite. Wigeon, Teal and Red-breasted Merganser can be found in good numbers here in the winter months and Common Scoter and Divers occasionally appear. Amongst the various waders to be found, Whimbrel are regular summer visitors.

The Duddon estuary holds many waders in winter, especially Oystercatcher, Curlew and Sanderling as well as wildfowl like Pintail, Wigeon and Grey-lag Geese. Sometimes Long-tailed Duck and various Divers appear. The large lake formed inside the sealed harbour and flooded mine workings at Hodbarrow is a very important site for the Red-breasted Merganser in the southern part of the county, as most birds in the region come here to moult in summer. It is also the breeding site of several species of Tern and Great-crested Grebes, a bird which is scarce in the county. Good numbers of diving duck frequent the area in winter. Unfortunately, the future of this site is in jeopardy as it is being developed as a holiday complex.

The Leven and Kent estuaries form the northern part of Morecambe Bay and as previously mentioned are important areas for waders and wildfowl in all seasons. These rivers, like most of the others in the county, have their resident Dipper, Common Sandpiper and Wagtail populations. Some, like the Eden and the Lune have Sand Martin colonies. Many of our rivers have experienced the welcome return of the Kingfisher after the disastrous decline in the 1962/3 winter. Another newcomer in recent years is the Goosander which has spread southwards through the county.

Lakes, Tarns and Reservoirs

The Lake District National Park, as the name implies, is an area of outstanding natural beauty with soft, yet impressive mountains and deep sparkling lakes. If you look carefully at a map of the area it is easy to imagine the lakes forming the 'spokes' of a wheel as they all point outward from the mass of the Cumbrian mountains. All the larger lakes are interesting for bird-life especially as a winter refuge for wildfowl. Bassenthwaite Water, Derwentwater and Ullswater all have good populations but Windermere is exceptional with 2% of the country's Tufted Duck and 5% of Goldeneye. This shows the importance of these lakes even though they are all under various recreational pressures.

Esthwaite Water is one of the few central lakes with a substantial reed-bed where waterfowl can breed; this includes

Great-crested Grebes. It is also one of the northernmost sites for breeding Reed Warblers.

Most of the larger lakes have got either, or both, Red-breasted Merganser or Goosander on them as a breeding species. The spread of these two saw-billed ducks has been a fairly spectacular development over the last fifteen years.

Several of the smaller tarns are outstanding due to their position in the county and as a consequence attract more unusual migrants, like Little Gull and Black Tern, almost annually. Two noteworthy tarns with this feature are Siddick Pond in the west and Sunbiggin Tarn in the east.

Siddick Pond is in the middle of the industrial west coast area and is open to regular persecution by egg collectors and 'cowboys' with air rifles, though it must be said that this is on the decrease since the site has been made a nature reserve by the local council with management by the CTNC. Here one may see Long-tailed Duck, Bewick's Swan or Short-eared Owl in winter, or Black Tern, Garganey or Grasshopper Warbler if you are a summer visitor.

Sunbiggin Tarn by contrast is in the heart of Westmorland moorland and stands at an altitude of 825 ft. It is situated on a migratory route between Morecambe Bay and the Eden Valley where the birds then fly either east to the East Coast and the Humber, or west to the Solway. Passage birds noted in recent years include Marsh Harrier, Black Tern and Red-necked Phalarope.

Reservoirs in the county have only recently been looked at as being of ornithological importance. Castle Carrock in the north, Ormsgill in the town of Barrow and Killington near Sedbergh in the south-east have produced interesting species like Divers, the rarer grebes, Osprey, and various other waders, wildfowl and terns.

Agriculture

Apart from the industrial area around Carlisle, Barrow and the mining towns on the west coast, Cumbria's main product is through its agriculture. The alluvial plain of the Solway with the Eden Valley and the coastal strip are the main areas for arable farming and the production of rootcrops. By far the largest part of the Cumbrian agricultural scene is in the rearing of livestock, especially sheep, dairy and beef cattle.

Sheep are bred on inland pastures and fell areas and are mainly of the local Swaledale and Herdwick breeds. During the winter months they are brought down from the harsh conditions on the high ground in the county to the valley bottoms and large estuarine saltmarshes.

The rich grassland areas, especially those overlaying limestone in the south of the county, is a habitat of relatively small undulating fields, with mature boundary hedges and ditches. These are valuable sites to many small birds like Linnet, Chaffinch and Whitethroat. The larger fields near the estuaries and coast of the county are important to species like Partridge, Lapwing and the now scarce Barn Owl. Sometimes these larger fields will produce a rarity like a Stone Curlew seen at Cartmel in 1976 and Quail in the valley of the River Crake in 1976 and around Grange-over-Sands in 1977.

With the modernised techniques of mechanical aids in agriculture and the inclination towards a monoculture in grassland there are still corners of fields and overgrown ponds and stoneheaps where brambles and thistles grow. This along with hedgerow trees like Ash, Sycamore, Holly and Rowan provide food and shelter for many birds. This counters the recent widespread use of herbicides, silage and mechanical hedge cutting etc. which inevitably have brought a reduction in the breeding population of birds like Lapwing, Partridge and Corn Bunting. By and large, the farming community are aware of the balance of nature they hold in their hands and it is hoped they will continue to do so.

Forest and Woodlands

The main areas of woodland occur in the Lake District National Park and to the north-east of the county near the Scottish border. In the latter site there are large tracts of conifers planted by the Forestry Commission on the Bewcastle Fells. In this corner of the county where relatively few ornithological records exist, one can expect to find exciting birds like Crossbills, Siskin and perhaps a rarity like a Goshawk.

Within the National Park both conifers and hardwoods are planted. Grizedale Forest is the main area here and the Forestry Commission have made tourism a feature by providing facilities like nature trails with observation hides and areas for picnic sites.

The hardwood areas of the forest produce birds like Redstart, Pied Flycatcher and Wood Warbler in the summer months, with migrant thrushes appearing in winter.

The coniferous areas have breeding Crossbill and Siskin. Of the scarcer birds of these woodlands, Hawfinch, Nuthatch and Lesser-spotted Woodpecker are noteworthy and can all be found in various districts.

Introductions released into Grizedale in recent years have included Capercaillie, Gadwall, Carolina Wood Duck, Golden and Reeve's Pheasants. Most of these birds have disappeared and whether the Forestry Commission keeps up this policy of introducing feral species is doubtful.

The Cumbrian woodlands are the northernmost range for breeding Marsh Tit and Chiffchaff as both these birds are local and scarce north of the border.

Moorland and Upland Fells

A large part of Cumbria is made up of upland habitat, whether it is the high grass and bracken covered fells in the south or the stony, peat plateaus of the Lakeland and Pennine mountains. The crags and cliffs of these mountainous regions find favour with Raven, Peregrine and in recent years the Golden Eagle, whereas the high plateaus of the Pennines are the habitat of Golden Plover, Dunlin and passage Dotterel. Regular breeding species of this area include Curlew, Wheatear, Meadow Pipit and Skylark. Red Grouse are common in the Pennines but scarce on the high ground of the Lake District. Black Grouse frequent the lower heather moorland localities like Geltsdale in the north and the Shap and Howgill Fells in the south.

Most of the breeding birds leave the high ground in winter, leaving small foraging flocks of Starlings, Redwing and Fieldfare to cover the lower slopes. With them can be found the odd party of Snow Bunting in the more severe conditions.

Large areas of moorland have been reclaimed in recent years by the forestry industry and in the young plantations can be found birds like Whinchat, Stonechat and Short-eared Owl.

The Lake District mountains and the Pennines are major attractions to many ramblers, fell-walkers and climbers. It is therefore a little surprising to find that human disturbance has not had more effect on the breeding success of birds like Ravens, Peregrine and more recently the return of the Golden Eagle. Even so, there are still many large areas of moorland that remain almost undisturbed throughout the year. It is here that you may find scarce birds like the Dotterel and Hen Harrier, species which were common breeding birds some two hundred years ago.

BIRD STUDY IN CUMBRIA

Morecambe Bay Wader Group

There are many pressures on the vast open expanse of sands and mudflats of Morecambe Bay as there is on all our estuarine habitats. The most important of these in recent years is the proposal to build a barrage to form a huge reservoir of water for the never ending needs of the increasing metropolis of central Lancashire. This is one of the many proposed barrage schemes throughout the country and to form a clear picture of the amount of birdlife that would be disrupted by these ideas the British Trust for Ornithology launched their Birds of the Estuaries Enquiry in 1969. It was soon realised that Morecambe Bay was the largest and one of the most important estuaries for birds in the British Isles. With the threat of the barrage proposal being most prominent, the Morecambe Bay Wader Group was formed to monitor wader migration and feeding habits in relation to the Bay.

To date over 25,000 waders have been ringed by the group, many of which have been recovered in Britain, Europe, Africa and even from the American continent. Many waders like Dunlin and Knot use the Bay as a 'staging post' where they stop and feed on their migration from Africa to Iceland and Greenland to breed. With so many waders being ringed and studied, the group has had many interesting long distance recoveries, some of which are recorded in the Systematic List. A detailed account of the group's studies can be found in 'The Birds of Morecambe Bay' by John Wilson.

Walney Bird Observatory

There are several features which make the South Walney Nature Reserve unique in the county. It has the only colony of Eiders on the west coast of England but is more widely known for the largest Herring/Lesser Black-backed Gull colony in Europe. A close study of the breeding activities of this colony is being done by the Animal Behaviour Department of Oxford University. Some of the results of this work have been published in Professor N Tinbergen's book 'The Herring Gull's World'.

It is a peninsula penetrating into Morecambe Bay, with the Irish Sea on its western coast. As such it is an ideal migration point for passage waders, sea-birds, and passerines. All this was realised in 1963 when the reserve was first formed.

Two Heligoland traps were built during the first two years of the reserve to note the movement of passage passerines. The first bird of note to be caught was a Melodious Warbler in 1964. This gave the needed inspiration to the formation of the Walney Bird Observatory. The following year the enthusiasm of the Observatory's small team of founder members was fired even further by the trapping of the third British specimen of an American White-throated Sparrow, this being the first one to be ringed in Europe.

The increase of the Gull colony had an adverse effect on migrating passerines, particularly in the Spring and numbers between 1967 and 1972 declined. This trend was reversed in 1973 when two more traps were built in the marsh area, since when the ringing totals have gradually increased.

To date many interesting species have been trapped and ringed at the Observatory, including several more Melodious Warblers, Firecrest, Red-breasted Flycatcher, Icterine, Barred, Yellow-browed and Pallas's Warblers and in 1982 a rarity from Asia in the form of a Paddyfield Warbler. Recoveries of Walney ringed birds have come from all over Europe, the more interesting being a Spotted Flycatcher recovered in Nigeria and remarkably a Long-eared Owl recovered on the Trans Siberian Railway in Russia. Of course there are many passage birds which pass through Walney without being caught and they include Marsh Harrier, Osprey, Hoopoe, Lapland Bunting and Shore Lark. Sea-watching has also become a regular part of the Observatory scene, especially since the erection of three hides during 1981/2. Leach's Petrel, Cory's and Sooty Shearwater, Little Auk and Grey Phalarope along with many sea-duck, divers, grebes, geese, gulls and terns have all been recorded.

During 1976 the marsh area was flooded purposely with the water level lowered in the Autumn to attract wading birds. A good variety of waders have been recorded at this site, the most noteworthy being Temminck's Stint, Spoonbill and an American Pectoral Sandpiper. The South Walney Nature Reserve has proved to be one of North-West England's important ornithological sites. This is enriched by the presence of the Observatory and its team of ringers and enthusiasts who already in its short life have verified this point.

Individual studies
Within the past twenty years the study of ornithology has increased at an incredible pace and many questions on

population and the migration of our birds have been studied. Unfortunately, Cumbria has been neglected to a greater extent by the professional ornithologist, but in recent years studies by local ornithologists have produced many interesting results and numerous new questions.

There are only a dozen or so people qualified to hold an 'A' or 'B' ringing licence working in the county; nevertheless, they are doing valuable work in gathering scientific data on both a county and national scale. Some of the species and areas under study at the present time include; Lake District Waterfowl (Miss K M Atkinson); Birds of Prey (G Horne); Dotterel, Siddick Pond (J C Callion); Sand Martins, Solway waders (M F Carrier); Terns and waders (J Sheldon); Walney birdlife (T Dean).

This only represents a small part of the wide range of potential habitat and species this rich county has to offer.

SYSTEMATIC LIST

Red throated Diver *(Gavia stellata)*   *Winter visitor*
This is the most regular species of the Diver family to be found off the Cumbrian coast. It occurs usually between the months of September and April. Numbers vary with between *two* and *four* birds being located in any one site, but small parties have been found during peak migration in March and April. During this period up to *ten* birds have been recorded on the Outer Solway, *twenty* off St Bees Head and *thirty-five* off Walney Island.

Inland records are much more unusual and birds recorded on rivers and lakes over the past twenty years include; *One,* 25 Feb-6 Mar, 1966, Coniston Water; *Two,* 22 Oct, 1973, Ullswater; *One,* 5-7 Mar, 1974, River Eden, between Musgrave and Sandford; *One,* 29 Dec, 1974, Killington Reservoir; *One,* 14 Oct, 1976, Bassenthwaite Water; *One,* 27 Oct, 1976, Blea Tarn; *One,* 11 Mar, 1979, Longtown gravel pits; *One,* 4 Apr, 1981, Wet Sleddale Dam, found dead; *One,* 27-30 Jan, 1982, River Derwent, Portinscale; *One,* 14 Nov, Derwentwater and *One,* 13-23 Mar, 1983, Haweswater.

Black throated Diver *(Gavia arctica)*   *Winter visitor*
This Diver has in the past been recorded as an irregular visitor to the coast with most birds being seen on inland lakes, tarns and reservoirs. With more methodical 'sea-watching' in recent years coastal records have increased substantially. Up to *three* birds were recorded between January and May in 1983 at South Walney and *three* birds were also recorded on the Outer Solway at Grune Point in mid-May of the same year. Other records in the period include a storm-bound bird found at Temple Sowerby in the Eden Valley in January 1970 and released on Ullswater; *One,* Jan, 1974, Arnside; *One,* 16-23 Jan, 1975; River Derwent Workington; *One,* 19 Jan, 1975, Windermere ferry with another at the same location 23 Mar, 1979; *One* between October and November 1976, Blelham Tarn; *One* in summer plumage on the sea, 28 Apr, 1976, St Bees; *One,* 2 Mar, 1979, River Kent, Kendal; *One,* 24-31 Dec, 1980, Killington reservoir; *One,* 9 Jan, 1981, Longtown gravel pits; *One,* 24-31 Mar, 1981, Cavendish Dock, Barrow; *Two,* 30 Apr, 1982, Newbiggin (Furness) and *One,* 13 Feb, 1983, Sandgate Marsh, Leven Estuary.

Great Northern Diver *(Gavia immer)* *Winter visitor*

In the past this bird was recorded more often on inland lakes than on the coast, but in more recent years it has been seen along the length of the Cumbrian coast more often. *Three* birds seen off South Walney, 23 Apr, 1967 were in summer plumage and a party of *seven* birds were seen at the same site by J Sheldon on 13 Apr, 1969.

Birds seen on inland waters during the period include;
One, 20 Mar, 1969, Windermere ferry (Miss K M Atkinson).
One, 4 Jan, 1970, Crummock Water.
One, 17 Nov, 1979, Elterwater (Miss K M Atkinson).
One, 16 Dec, 1979, Killington reservoir (A F Gould, I Kinley).
One, 19 Mar, 1979, Wastwater (M Madders).
One, 8 Jan, 1981, Longtown gravel pits (R Armstrong, M Ramsden).
One, 17 Dec, 1981, Wray Castle, Lake Windermere (R Schofield).
One, 9 Jan, 1984, off Belle Isle, Lake Windermere (H Fletcher).

Pied-billed Grebe *(Podilymbus podiceps)* *Vagrant*

Details of a bird of this secretive American species were claimed by R Armstrong, M Ramsden and M F Carrier at Oakbank gravel pit, Longtown on 18-25 Sep, 1982.

This record is subject to acceptance by British Birds Rarities Committee at the date of going to press.

Little Grebe *(Tachybaptus ruficollis)* *Resident*

A regular breeding bird throughout the county in suitable reed-covered sites. Birds often move to estuarine and coastal sites during the winter months. Large numbers sometimes occur at these sites such as *forty one* birds, 22 Sep, 1974 at Hodbarrow on the Duddon Estuary and *forty* birds, 4 Dec, 1983, at Cavendish Dock, Barrow.

Great crested Grebe *(Podiceps cristatus)* *Uncommon resident and winter visitor*

The first record of breeding success of this bird occurred in 1908, since then it attempted to breed on several lakes in the central lakes area. Favourable habitat for it seems to be scarce as the few regular sites include Bassenthwaite Water, Overwater, Esthwaite Water and Urswick Tarn in Furness. It has nested on other lakes and reservoirs but this does not seem to build up to a regular pattern, possibly due to lack of cover, irregular water levels and disturbance. The BTO Great crested Grebe survey conducted in 1975 revealed that there were only *seven* successful breeding pairs in the county which compared to the amount of open water sites shows just how scarce this bird is

In winter months it is regularly found on coastal and estuarine locations. Records at this time sometimes involve large numbers such as *ten* birds, 9 Sep, 1973 on the Kent Estuary by Arnside Viaduct; *sixty,* 31 Jan, 1976, Cavendish Dock; and *thirty one,* 20 July, 1981, off Foulney Island.

Red-necked Grebe *(Podiceps grisegena)   Scarce winter migrant*
An irregular winter visitor, being seen most frequently on coastal and estuarine sites of the Solway in the north and Morecambe Bay between the Leven and Duddon estuaries in the south. It has also appeared on some of the larger lakes during the period like Coniston Water and Lake Windermere.

A bird in full summer plumage was seen 15-19 Apr, 1975 on Ormsgill Reservoir, Barrow (J Richardson) with another in the same garb 16 Apr, 1978 on Killington Reservoir (M Hutcheson). *Two* birds were seen together 19-23 Feb, 1979 on Ulverston Canal (A J Mackenzie, W Kydd) during a severe spell of weather, and *one* was present from 12 Nov, 1983 until 16 Jan, 1984 at Siddick Pond, Workington (J C Callion).

Slavonian Grebe *(Podiceps auritus)   Scarce winter migrant*
Records over the period come from coastal, estuarine and inland waters. Single birds are usually seen but *two* together were found 3 Jan, 1983 on the Irt Estuary (A Strand).

The breeding range of this bird in Scotland is slowly spreading southwards and to date has reached Perthshire. It is interesting to note a bird in full summer dress 23-26 Jul, 1977 on Wet Sleddale Dam (Miss K M Atkinson *et al).*

Black-necked Grebe *(Podiceps nigricollis)   Scarce winter migrant*
Most records of this bird are found between October and March and come from coastal and estuarine sites. A scattering of sightings have occurred on inland waters between July and September. Single birds are usually seen, but *three* were seen 3 Feb, 1968 on Castle Carrock Reservoir (G Horne).

This grebe bred in the old county of Westmorland in 1935 (Stokoe, BLC). Single birds in summer dress were recorded in the Sunbiggin Tarn area during the period 1968-1975. Although breeding was suspected in 1968, this was not confirmed (Cumbria Bird Reports 1970-75).

Fulmar *(Fulmarus glacialis)*   *Breeding and summer migrant*
The Fulmar first bred on the cliffs of St Bees Head as recently as 1940 (Stokoe, BLC). The colony is steadily expanding, a feature which seems to be widespread throughout the country. Two hundred occupied sites were recorded in 1975, but this figure fluctuates from year to year (Cumbria Bird Report 1975).

Birds are regularly seen along the length of the Cumbrian coastline between March and October, with winter records being not so frequent.

Inland records are scarce and are usually reported after severe Autumn gales. Records during the period include a bird flying south over Ratherheath Tarn, Kendal, 1 Sep, 1973; *one* picked up in a poor condition, Ambleside, 26 Sep, 1979; *one* over Houghton, Carlisle, 30 Apr, 1981 and *one* flying south over Tindale Tarn, 12 Jul, 1982.

A corpse of an arctic 'blue phase' Fulmar was picked up at Sandscale, 10 Mar, 1967 by K Brown.

Cory's Shearwater *(Calonectris diomedea)*   *Rare passage migrant*
With the increasing coverage given to watching sea-bird movements along the coast, more records of this bird and other rare sea-birds will probably come to light in the future. Although not mentioned in Stokoe's BLC, the following records have been accepted during the period.

One flying south, off Walney Island, 9 Aug, 1972 (K Brown) (LBR 72, No 64)

All the other records come from Walney Bird Observatory and are;

Two, 17 Aug, with *singles* 13 and 27 Sep, 1980.

Two flying north, 16 Jun, 1981.

Five flying south, 8 Aug, 1982.

Two flying north, 6 Sep with another *two,* 11 Sep, 1983.

Great Shearwater *(Puffinus gravis)*   *Rare passage migrant*
Although sightings of several large Shearwaters have been noted in the period, probably the first confirmed record of

Great Shearwater was seen off St Bees Head, on 9 and 27 Jul, 1974 (RSPB). Other records since that date include;
One, Inner Solway, 7 May, 1978 (M F Carrier).
One, St Bees Head, 28 May, 1979 (RSPB).
One, Walney Bird Observatory, 20 Sep, 1982.
One flying north, Walney Bird Observatory, 19 Sep, 1983.

Sooty Shearwater *(Puffinus griseus)*   *Scarce passage migrant*
Like the previous *two* Shearwaters, the Sooty Shearwater is not mentioned in Stokoe's BLC. However, since the first record of *two* birds off Walney Island, 18 Apr, 1965 (W H Tickle), the bird has been recorded almost annually along the coast between Walney and St Bees Head. They have been recorded in the period April and July to October and usually appear as singletons, although *six* were seen together on 18 Sep, 1983 at Walney Bird Observatory where a winter bird was recorded on 26 Feb, 1982.

Manx Shearwater *(Puffinus puffinus)*   *Passage migrant*
This is a regular Spring and Autumn passage migrant along the Cumbrian coast, with most birds being seen during Jul/Aug. Numbers vary from year to year, but *two hundred and four* seen off Walney on 3 Sep, 1970 was unusual.
    Inland records are rare, occurring during or after adverse weather conditions. This makes the following records noteworthy;
    A corpse, Sandy Bottoms, Kendal, 21 Sep, 1981, with a second bird being found at Kentrigg, Kendal, three days later. This bird died the following day (A F Gould).
    A bird picked up at Underley House Farm, Kirkby Lonsdale, 20 Aug, 1982, was released at Silverdale (Lancs) (B Foxton). A bird seen resting on the estuary sands at Meathop Marsh, 26 Aug, 1982, before flying off westwards, was possibly the same bird (J Greenwood).
    The pale Balearic race *(P. puffinus mauretanicus)*, has been seen at Walney Bird Observatory twice to date. *One,* 3 Mar, 1982 and *two,* 10 Sep, 1983.

White-faced or **Frigate Petrel** *(Pelagodroma marina)*
A bird described in detail in Macpherson's 'Fauna of Lakeland' and Stokoe's BLC is no longer accepted.

Wilson's Petrel *(Oceanites oceanicus)*   *Vagrant*
Stokoe's BLC mentions three occurrences in the county of this rarity. All shore-line corpses, being found at Castlesteads in

1881, Walney in 1890 and Allonby Nov, 1932. Unfortunately the Walney record is no longer accepted (*Ibis* 109, 2: p 158).

Storm Petrel *(Hydrobates pelagicus) Uncommon Autumn passage migrant*

Although this bird is not recorded annually, it does occur between September and December especially after a period of westerly gales. In severe weather conditions birds may be 'wrecked' well inland, such as in 1952 when birds were picked up inland as far as the Pennines (Lakeland Birds, 1958).

Records for the period are sparse except for early October 1983 after a period of prolonged gales. They include; *One* found dead on the shoreline of Little Langdale Tarn, July 1968 (per Westmorland Gazette); *One* found dead, 7 Aug, 1970, Walney Lighthouse; *One* flying down Solway, 17 Sep, 1974, Drumburgh (CBR 1974); *One,* 7 Aug, 1975, Workington harbour (CBR 77/78); *One* watched in the centre of the lake by yachtsmen, 14 Sep, 1980, Millerground, Lake Windermere (D Thompson); Tide-line corpse, 23 Nov, 1981, North Walney (L H Sanderson); *Two,* 14 Jun, 1983, Walney Bird Observatory; *One,* 14 Oct, 1983, Grune Point (S Turnbull); *One* flying inland, 16 Oct, 1983, Kirksanton (A F Gould); *One* over the fields, 16 Oct, 1983, Far Arnside (J B Todd).

Leach's Petrel *(Oceanodroma leucorrhoa)*   *Irregular Autumn passage migrant*

Like the last species, the Leach's Petrel is a bird which is seen along the coast during Autumn gales. It has been recorded more frequently than the Storm Petrel and appears to get 'funnelled' into Morecambe Bay during prolonged storm conditions (Birds of Lancaster and District, 1968-79). Details of 'wrecks' in 1952 and 1963 appear in the Field Naturalist, Vol 8, No 4.

Records for the period include *one* over Lake Windermere, 29 Sep, 1963 (C H D Acland) with a corpse found the same day at Grune Point, Solway. Another corpse was found nearby on Skinburness Marsh, 19 Nov, 1971 (J Pope). An unusual Spring record came from the Solway with a bird off Burgh Marsh, 6 Apr, 1976 (M B Leakey). A corpse was found, 14 Nov, 1977, Biggar Bank, Walney Island (W H Tickle). Walney Bird Observatory recorded *singles* on 20 and 27 Sep, 1979 and *four* on 13 Sep, 1980. October gales in 1983 brought the highest number of records since the 'wreck' of 1952 with *two* over Siddick Pond, 16 Oct; *One* off Workington pier, 18 Oct (both J C Callion); *One* off Kirksanton Haws, 16 Oct (A F Gould) and *one* at Kents Bank, Grange over Sands, 18 Oct (P Satterthwaite).

Walney Bird Observatory had a notable movement during this period with *singles,* 9 and 20 Sep, 12 and 25 Oct, *two,* 5 Sep, and *nine,* 8 and 18 Oct. *One* was also seen here 29 Oct, 1984.

Gannet *(Sula bassana)*   *Summer passage bird*

The Gannet can be seen regularly as a passage migrant between mid-April and October. The numbers of birds seen has increased during the period, with the occasional large party of birds being seen. Examples being *c four hundred,* 8 Jun, 1976, off Haverigg Point, *one hundred and two,* 30 Aug, 1967 and *c three hundred and fifty,* 28 Aug, 1976, off Walney Island.

Bad weather conditions bring birds into the Solway and Morecambe Bay, with prolonged adverse conditions bringing birds up the estuaries and well inland. Records in the period of storm-bound birds include an immature bird found at Renwick in the Pennine foothills and released on Ullswater, 25 Sep, 1975; *One* found dead in a field, Great Orton, Carlisle, 20 Sep, 1976; An immature bird seen flying west down Haweswater, 5 Jun, 1976, being seen by a second observer over Nan Bield Pass and by possibly a third observer the next day at Blakeholme, Lake Windermere; *One* came up with the flood-tide on the Upper Kent estuary, 23 May, 1982 and rested on a sandbank at Foulshaw; *One* found having hit overhead wires at Linstock, Carlisle, 4 Sep, 1983; *One* at Whinfell Tarn, near Kendal, 19 Oct, 1983 was found dead the next day.

Cormorant *(Phalacrocorax carbo)*   *Resident and passage migrant*

For such a common bird on the coast, estuaries and large inland lakes, it is rather scarce as a breeding bird in the county. Non-breeding birds are present most of the year to which numbers are increased greatly by wintering individuals. During the winter birds are found well inland, often small numbers reaching the River Eden and the Pennines.

Most of the lakes have cormorants during the winter, with numbers of up to one hundred on the larger lakes. Here the habit of tree-roosting is commonplace. The largest totals come from the Solway and around Barrow-in-Furness, where *two hundred* plus birds can be found on Cavendish Dock.

Birds ringed on the Clyde, Forth and Farne Islands have been recovered in the county during the last twenty years.

Shag *(Phalacrocorax aristotelis)*   *Irregular visitor*

Surprisingly the Shag is not seen regularly along the Cumbrian coast, although in recent years a few birds, mainly immatures, have appeared during the summer months around St Bees Head. At Walney Bird Observatory it is not common with single birds appearing usually in the winter months.

It is rarely found inland with a bird appearing on the River Eden at Appleby, 20-26 Mar, 1974 with another on the same river at Ormside, 13 Dec, 1976.

Two were on Lake Windermere, 21 Nov, 1974 with an immature on the same lake, 16 Jan, 1980 and *two* more, 19 Jan and 13 Mar, 1981. Most unusual were *seven* birds found on Blelham Tarn, 17 Jan, 1980, after a period of westerly gales (Miss K M Atkinson).

Bittern *(Botaurus stellaris)*   *Scarce irregular visitor*

With a small increase during the period of the Bittern at the RSPB reserve at Leighton Moss, just south of the county, one can only speculate that this bird could be seen more often around Cumbrian lakes and tarns in future.

Records occur mainly during the autumn and winter months and usually feature immature birds. There are sixteen reports noted in the last twenty years from a wide area of the county (CBR 1970-84). Noteworthy records include *two* at Whinfell Tarn, near Kendal, 8 Aug, 1974, a site with five records in the period. *One,* 24 Jan, 1984 at Walney Bird Observatory was the first record there.

Little Bittern *(Ixobrychus minutus)*   *Vagrant*

One old record. A female shot on the River Petteril, near Carlisle, July 1847.

Night Heron *(Nycticorax nycticorax)*   *Rare passage migrant*

Stokoe's BLC mentions six records of this rare heron, mainly immatures. A bird frequented the River Eden in the Appleby area from October 1970 until March 1972. It is possible that this bird was of captive origin (R W Robson, G G Wood *et al*). The most recent record is of an immature bird seen on Thurstonfield Lough, 4 Apr, 1976.

Squacco Heron *(Ardeola ralloides)*   *Vagrant*
An old record on the River Eden at Lazonby, June 1845.

Cattle Egret *(Bubulcus ibis)*   *Vagrant*
It is rather unusual that the only records of this bird occurred within three weeks of each other, giving rise to the possibility that just *one* bird was involved. The first bird was found feeding in a hayfield at New Hall, Appleby on 3 Jul, 1964 (Miss C W Hull, R W Robson). The second arrived at Walney Bird observatory 26 Jul, 1964 (T K Bradshaw, F Quale). Both records were accepted by BBRC.

Cattle Egret

Little Egret *(Egretta garzetta)*   *Rare migrant*
Four of five records for the county occurred on the Solway, all of them being recorded in the last twenty years.

One present from 26 Dec, 1973-16 Mar, 1974 in the Bowness-on-Solway area was seen by several members of the Carlisle Natural History Society. This is a very unusual record in that very few birds have been known to over-winter in Britain.

One present 29 May, 1975, Rockcliffe Marsh, with large Gulls (D & J Bailey).

One, 3 and 4 Jun, 1981, Border Marsh (G Horne).

One, 26-28 Jun, 1981, Dunnerholme Marsh, Duddon Estuary (B Pickthall, S C Peter, I Young *et al*).

One, 3 Jun, 1984, Carr Beds, Rockcliffe (A Cremin).

Grey Heron *(Ardea cinerea)*   *Breeding resident*

The Grey Heron is well distributed throughout the county, occurring on most estuaries, rivers, lakes and tarns. It often frequents the coast in winter and has been recorded at fairly high altitudes on small streams in the fells and on the Pennines.

It is still persecuted in some areas and for that reason alone it would be unwise to list traditional nesting sites.

During the severe winter of 1964 the population in the county dropped, but by 1970 numbers were back to normal and tended to expand as by 1975 new small heronries were located in the Duddon, Rusland and Kent valleys.

Macpherson states that some heronries have been established for over 300 years, an example being the heronry at Muncaster which was regularly visited in 1621 for food and the most famous Lakeland heronry at Dallam Tower was recorded by the naturalist Bewick for dispute over nesting territory between herons and rooks from the nearby rookery.

Purple Heron *(Ardea purpurea)*   *Vagrant*

An old record of a bird near Alston, 1850.

White Stork *(Ciconia ciconia)*   *Rare migrant*

There have been seven records of White Stork in Cumbria in the last twenty years, making a total of eleven in all.

One around the Leven Estuary from 7 Apr-28 May, 1967 (H Fooks).

Two landed on a flat garage roof, Kenmount Place, Carlisle, 14 Apr, 1968 (Carlisle NHS).

One, 25 May, 1976, Tarn House Tarn, Kirkby Stephen (R & D Baines).

One, 29 May, 1978, Shap (Miss R Pheasey, B J Rafferty).

One, 3-6 Jun, 1979, Sebergham and Brocklebank, near Wigton (R K Jones).

One, 25 June-3 Aug, 1981, Rockcliffe Marsh (Misses S Grieg and M Holloway, D Bailey).

One, 25-26 Apr, 1984, Crosscanonby (Miss M M Milne), same, 27 Apr, 1984, Silloth Golf Course (P. Baker).

All, except the 1967 and 1968 records, have been submitted to the BBRC and have been accepted.

Glossy Ibis *(Plegadis falcinellus)*   *Vagrant*

Two old records; *One* near Carlisle, Sept 1921 and *one* on Gilsland moors Nov 1932.

Spoonbill *(Platalea leucorodia)*   *Rare summer visitor*

Stokoe's BLC lists seven records. There have been a further seven records over the period of the last twenty years, all of which, except one, have been on or near to Morecambe Bay.

One, 10-20 Oct, 1966, Walney Bird Observatory.

Two, 10 May, 1970, Kent Estuary (LDBS report).

One, 21 May, 1970, Siddick Pond, Workington (R Stokoe)

One, 21 Jul, 1970, Walney Bird Observatory.

Two, 19-28 Jul, 1972, Kent Estuary (Miss J Atkinson, B Fereday, M Hutcheson).

One, 6-19 Aug, 1976, Kent Estuary (A F Gould, I Kinley, D B Thexton).

Three, 8-11 Jun, 1982, Walney Bird Observatory.

Mute Swan *(Cygnus olor)*   *Breeding resident*

For a county of many lakes and tarns, the Mute Swan is not as common a bird as one might expect. the BTO Mute Swan Survey for 1978 records only *twenty two* breeding pairs in the vice-counties of Westmorland and Furness, with only a slight increase in 1983 with *twenty eight* pairs. Birds can be found on lowland lakes over an acre in size, canals and rivers. Cavendish Dock, Barrow is a well known site for this species to moult and flocks of around *one hundred* birds can be found in July and August. Smaller moulting flocks can also be found at Siddick Pond on the coast and Longtown gravel pits in the north.

Bewick's Swan *(Cygnus bewickii)*   *Scarce passage migrant*

This is not a common swan in the county with most records coming from the Solway. March seems to be the best month to find these birds, probably the Irish wintering population returning to their breeding grounds in the Arctic.

Large herds in recent years include *twenty four* on River Esk, near Gretna, from 22 Feb-2 Mar, 1975; *nineteen,* 13 Nov, 1976, Walney Bird Observatory; *twenty four* →S, 12 Nov, 1983, over Coniston and *sixteen* →N, 27 Mar, 1984, over Kendal.

Whooper Swan *(Cygnus cygnus)*   *Winter visitor*

This is a regular visitor to many inland waters between October and April. Numbers usually involve between two and six birds, often a family party. Many inland waters are visited with birds being found on estuaries and the coast in hard conditions. Some sites have become traditional wintering areas and these include Tindale Tarn; Siddick

Pond, Workington; Grasmere; Elterwater and Tarn House Tarn, Kirkby Stephen. The Eden Valley often has large herds of up to *one hundred and twenty* birds in two sites, namely the Linstock area in the north or between Lazonby and Kirkby Thore to the east.

Bean Goose *(Anser fabalis)*   *Scarce winter visitor*
This used to be the common grey goose of the Solway, but now has become a rarity. A bird shot out of a party of twelve, 4 Nov, 1974, on Burgh Marsh, was retained by the Tullie House Museum, Carlisle and is probably the first record in a period of thirty years. Other records in the period include *one* found dead on South Walney, 5 Mar, 1969; *One,* 26 Oct, 1982 with Grey-lag, at Culgaith; *sixteen* →W 27 Oct, 1982 at Tindale Tarn; *Five,* 30 Jan, 1983 at Langwathby and *one,* 18 Nov, 1983 at Walney Bird Observatory.

Pink-footed Goose *(Anser brachyrhynchus)   Winter visitor and*
passage migrant
Although numbers of this bird have risen on the Solway marshes during peak passage periods, it fluctuates as a winter visitor to the county.

The coastal and southern estuaries have a few birds each winter, usually small numbers and often with wintering Grey-lag flocks. Flocks of more than *thirty* birds is unusual, except during severe conditions and recent noteworthy occurrences include; *c one thousand,* 31 Dec, 1981, Eskmeals Marsh; *three hundred and thirteeen,* 17 Jan, 1982, Duddon Estuary; *c three hundred,* Jan-late May, 1982, Leven Estuary; *sixty four,* 30 Jan, 1983, West Plain, Flookburgh; *ninety,* 15-16 Feb, 1983, Walney Bird Observatory.

In recent years there has been a big increase in the winter population in West Lancashire salt-marshes and passage of large skeins along the Cumbrian coast between Solway and Ribble is regular. In good weather conditions skeins will often traverse a line over the Lake District mountains, the most favoured route being Bassenthwaite and Dunmail to Lake Windermere and on towards Morecambe Bay.

During March numbers can reach up to *five thousand* birds on the Solway marshes as the birds gather prior to moving on to their breeding grounds. *Seven thousand* birds on Rockcliffe Marsh during March/April 1976 was exceptional.

Inland the bird is scarce and *nine,* 3 Nov, 1974 at Culgaith in the Eden Valley and *four,* 17 Nov, 1977 at Sunbiggin Tarn was unusual.

White-fronted Goose *(Anser albifrons)*   *Scarce winter visitor*
Both the European race *(A. albifrons albifrons)* and the
Greenland race *(A. albifrons flavirostris)* visit Cumbria
intermittently. Records usually consist of single birds in other
visiting flocks of 'grey' geese, sometimes *three* or *four* birds are
seen together.

Larger flocks seen in the period include: *twenty-four,* 18 Jan,
1970 over Coniston; *fourteen,* 4 Dec, 1982, Walney Bird
Observatory; *six,* 6 Feb, 1983, Skirwith, Eden Valley.
Greenland birds include *five,* 27 Oct-20 Nov, 1970, Walney
Bird Observatory; *four,* 13-30 Dec, 1980, Kirksanton Haws.

Grey-lag Goose *(Anser anser)*   *Winter visitor and feral breeding resident*
The Grey-lag is the most frequently found goose in Cumbria.
Winter migrants can be found in large numbers on the Solway
and in the Eden Valley with smaller numbers wintering on
Morecambe Bay. Feral birds have been introduced and breed
regularly in Central Lakeland, in the Duddon Valley and
around the Ravenglass area, although numbers are not high.

Around *three hundred* birds winter on the Solway and
Morecambe Bay areas but there has been a significant
increase in recent years in the Eden Valley population to
around a maximum of *two thousand* birds, a record of *c two
thousand, one hundred and fifty* at Staingills on 3 Mar, 1977 being
the highest to date.

Snow Goose *(Anser caerulescens)*
It is impossible to determine the true status of this bird in
Britain as it is kept in many British and European waterfowl
collections and escapes are quite frequent.

A pair which attempted to breed on Haweswater in 1982
and 1983 were obvious escapes.

Single birds are occasionally seen with wintering Grey-lag
with *four* birds in this situation at Culgaith, 16 Feb, 1983.
A blue phase Lesser Snow Goose was found with Barnacle
Geese, 19 Apr, 1983 on Rockcliffe Marsh.

Canada Goose *(Branta canadensis)*   *Resident and passage migrant.*
This bird was introduced into the county as recently as the
mid-1950's and has expanded into several sizeable flocks.
Stokoe BLC gives full detail of this introduction.

To date the birds have become established in three main
groups, each containing around a *hundred* birds. They can be

found in the Derwentwater/Crummock/Thirlmere area, the Eden Valley and around Killington Reservoir in the south. The breeding success of the resident flocks vary from year to year. 1976 was a particularly poor year as the drought conditions of that summer lowered water-tables to such an extent that the breeding islands on the various waters used by the birds became accessible to predators.

Movement of non-breeding birds can be seen over a wide area of the county, some examples being *fifty-five* moving west on 14 Jun, 1974, seen over Kendal and Arnside and *eighty-eight* moving south-west on 26 Jul, 1976, being seen over Rydal, Ambleside, Windermere, Levens and Milnthorpe. Passage migrants increase the resident population in Spring and Autumn, particularly in the Eden Valley where a maximum figure of *three hundred and thirty* birds were seen at Temple Sowerby on 24 Oct, 1982. Local Wildfowling Societies recently attempted to introduce the Canada Goose on to sites where they as yet have not occurred. An example of this being twenty-one birds introduced on a pond at Mawbray in Spring 1975, but by 30 Dec only *four* birds were left.

Barnacle Goose *(Branta leucopsis)*   *Winter visitor*
In the past decade, Barnacle Geese have been increasing annually in the numbers visiting the Solway during the winter months. In most winters, the Solway flock moves on to the English shore during the latter half of the season, where numbers build up prior to their departure to their breeding grounds in Spitzbergen. The peak count to date has been around *eight thousand* birds recorded during late March 1981. Quite often birds will linger well into the Spring. *Two* late birds remained until 9 Jun, 1973 on Rockcliffe Marsh.

Small flocks will often 'overshoot' the Solway on their arrival in the Autumn and can be found at various coastal sites. *Forty-five,* 7 Oct, 1974, Meathop Marsh, Kent Estuary; *fifty-three,* 30 Nov, 1980, Haverigg; *twenty-one,* 30 Sep, 1981, Biggar Bank, Walney; and *forty,* 15 Nov, 1982, Sandscale Haws being just a few examples.

Several feral Barnacle Geese can be found in various localities throughout the county during the Summer months. An interesting record of *three* birds seen on the Upper Kent Estuary, 21-28 Aug, 1983. The birds were ringed and *one* was identified as being ringed by the Wildfowl Trust at Arundel, Sussex during 1982, last being seen there in December of that year.

Brent Goose *(Branta bernicla)*   *Scarce winter visitor*

Although an irregular visitor to all the estuaries in the county, a small family group has been visiting the Walney/Foulney Island area for the past six winters. Numbers in this group are slowly growing with *twenty-one,* 16-21 Apr, 1983 being the maximum to date. These birds are the dark bellied race *(B. bernicla bernicla),* which normally winters in S.E. England.

Away from the coastal sites stragglers occasionally appear with the 'grey' geese inland. Usually *single* birds are involved but *two,* 28 Feb, 1974 and *three,* 14 Oct, 1978 both at Bolton in the Eden Valley, with Grey-lag are noteworthy.

Ruddy Shelduck *(Tadorna ferruginea)*

Stokoe notes two old records. As this is a popular bird in many wildfowl collections the possibility of sightings being of genuine wild birds is small. However a *single* bird, 31 Aug-1 Sep, 1983 on Burgh Marsh on the Solway and *one,* 27 Jul-11 Aug, 1983 at Sandside, Kent Estuary is interesting.

Shelduck *(Tadorna tadorna)*   *Resident and passage migrant*

A common bird on all estuarine habitat round the Cumbrian coastline. Large numbers can be found, especially in winter, on the Solway and on Morecambe Bay where peak numbers can reach *three thousand* birds. Most of the Shelduck population in the county migrates to the Heligoland Bight during the mid-summer months to moult leaving a few adults with the current year's immature birds. On return from the moulting grounds birds will often occur in small numbers on inland lakes and tarns.

Birds often move several miles inland away from the estuarine feeding grounds to breed, although the Shelduck no longer breeds on Lake Windermere as referred to by Stokoe BLC. The last positive breeding record here was in 1970 when nine young were seen.

Wigeon *(Anas penelope)*   *Winter visitor and passage migrant*

A common winter visitor with the largest numbers occurring on the Solway, the Duddon and around Walney Island. It also appears regularly on lower inland lakes and tarns, especially Bassenthwaite. Peak numbers occur in Spring and Autumn.

A small number of Wigeon breed annually in the north-east of the county in various habitats from a coastal moss to an upland tarn.

Gadwall *(Anas strepera)*   *Scarce resident and winter visitor*

The Gadwall has managed to establish itself in small numbers in a few areas in recent years. With known introductions in the Grizedale Forest area in 1975, the actual number of wild birds is vague. A small breeding population has built up in the upper Eden Valley. Elsewhere, the bird is irregular usually occurring in single figures, although *twenty-three,* 24 Jul, 1977 at Sunbiggin Tarn was exceptional.

Teal *(Anas crecca)*   *Resident, winter visitor*

A common winter visitor with large numbers occurring around Walney Island. Smaller numbers occur on the Solway and the Duddon, with a few birds wintering on most estuarine sites and lower inland waters.

It is a sparse and scattered breeding bird with nest sites varying from coastal salt-marshes to upland moorland.

An American Green-winged Teal *(A. crecca carolinensis)* was shot at Levens, December 1936.

Mallard *(Anas platyrhynchos)*   *Resident and passage migrant*

This is a common and successful breeding duck throughout the county, thriving in suitable habitat from the coast to around the 1,000 ft. level in the fells.

Numbers build up with passage birds during October and March, but peak figures often occur in mid-winter when most of the population congregates on inland waters. Most of the passage birds come from a wide area of Northern Europe, a typical example being a bird ringed 16 Nov, 1979 at Fano, Denmark was shot 29 Dec, 1979 at Melmerby, a distance of 709 km.

Pintail *(Anas acuta)*   *Winter visitor and passage migrant*

This is a scarce breeding bird with only a handful of records in the last twenty years. Individual pairs nested in the Solway area during 1973, 1976 and 1982 with other records coming from the Leven Estuary in 1965 and Furness in 1983.

Winter numbers vary from year to year, but in a 'Pintail' year large numbers can congregate on Cumbrian estuaries, particularly the Duddon and around Morecambe Bay. Peak figures include *c two thousand,* 24 Dec, 1962 on Duddon; *c one thousand two hundred,* 24 Nov, 1969 on the Flookburgh marshes; *c one thousand one hundred,* 14 Oct, 1984 off Grange-over-Sands. Numbers have been increasing at this latter site since they were first recorded there in 1973.

Inland records are infrequent and usually involve *pairs* or *single* birds, so *ten* birds seen on 28 Sep, 1977 at Tarn House Tarn, Kirkby Stephen was unusual.

Garganey *(Anas querquedula)*   *Scarce passage migrant*
Although this bird is recorded as a regular but sparse breeding species in neighbouring counties, no breeding records have come to light in Cumbria to date.

Of the twenty-four reports of this bird over the last twenty years most have occurred in the Spring and August and usually involves a *pair* or *single* birds. *Three* birds have been observed on three occasions at Siddick Pond, Workington. Most of the records come from estuarine and freshwater sites within 10 km of the coast.

Shoveler *(Anas clypeata)*   *Winter visitor and passage migrant*
Over the past decade this duck has decreased as a breeding bird, restricting itself to the lowland north-western part of the county. Elsewhere it is an infrequent winter visitor from mid-August until April.

It has been recorded on most inland waters and estuaries in small numbers. Some recent larger gatherings include: *c two hundred and fifty,* Oct, 1971 at Selker Bay; *c one hundred,* 3 Oct, 1974, Leven Estuary; *thirty-two,* 20th Dec, 1976, Siddick Pond, Workington and *c forty,* 13 Aug, 1983, Helton Tarn, Witherslack. The last record occurred during a period of drought and a lot of mud was exposed at the site.

Red-crested Pochard *(Netta rufina)*   *Vagrant*
Stokoe cites two old records. Although it is difficult to verify a genuine wild bird of this species, as many are kept in captivity, the following records have occurred over the last twenty years: A drake on Lake Windermere, May to Sep, 1967; A drake, 20 Oct, 1970 on Cavendish Dock, Barrow-in-Furness and a *pair,* 10-15 Sep, 1978, Tarn House Tarn, Kirkby Stephen.

Pochard *(Aythya ferina)*   *Winter visitor and passage migrant*
This is a rare breeding bird in the county, the only record during the period being a *pair* seen with *four* juveniles, 14 Aug, 1980 on Sunbiggin Tarn. A few birds 'summer' on sites like Siddick Pond, Hodbarrow, Millom and around the Barrow-in-Furness area.

Most birds come between September and April with peak numbers occurring in November. Flocks of around *two hundred and fifty* birds occur regularly on Cavendish Dock, Barrow and on some of the largest lakes in the county.

Ring-necked Duck *(Aythya collaris)*   *Vagrant*
This American duck has been appearing in the British Isles regularly since 1977, so the first county records, of possibly the same drake, were not too unexpected.
Drake, 4-7 Apr, 1982, Sunbiggin Tarn (S T Robinson, I Kinley *et al*).
Drake, 9-12 Apr, 1982, Chapel Rigg Tarn, Newbiggin-on-Lune (R & D Baines).
Drake, 2-5 May, 1982, Esthwaite Water (G L Agar, W Davison, R S Wimpress).

Ferruginous Duck *(Aythya nyroca)*   *Vagrant*
The first county records occurred during the period.
Drake, 27 Sep-14 Oct, 1962, Foulney Island (J Sheldon A James *et al*)
Drake, 28 Oct, 1967, Cavendish Dock, Barrow-in-Furness (J Sheldon)

Tufted Duck *(Aythya fuligula)*   *Resident and winter visitor*
Although this duck breeds in small numbers in the county where the habitat is suitable, the population is substantially increased with migrant winter visitors between September and March. It occurs as a breeding bird on reservoirs, lakes and tarns up to 1,000 ft. In winter flocks are found at lower levels and it is rarely found on the sea except in severe conditions.

Peak numbers usually occur in November when some recent high totals include: *one hundred and sixty-three,* 6 Nov, 1977 on Bassenthwaite Water; *three hundred and forty-six* 22 Nov, 1979, Lake Windermere and *four hundred and forty-five,* 23 Oct, 1982 on Cavendish Dock, Barrow.

SL.

Ring-necked and Tufted Duc

Scaup *(Aythya marila)*   *Winter visitor*
Stokoe refers to large flocks of Scaup on the Solway and Leven Estuary on Morecambe Bay during the winter months.

On the Solway a few birds stay all summer and peak during the winter months to around *four hundred and fifty* birds, with *c nine hundred and seventy,* 2 Nov, 1982 at Cardurnock (M F Carrier) being the highest count in the period. On the Leven, numbers now rarely reach *one hundred* birds, but *one hundred and twenty,* 20 Mar, 1970, off Bardsea was noteworthy, with *one hundred and forty-two* here on 14 Jan, 1984.

It occurs elsewhere around the coast in small numbers and is frequently seen off Drigg, on Hodbarrow, Duddon, around Walney Island and on Cavendish Dock.

It is scarce inland, but has appeared on tarns, lakes and reservoirs between September and April and usually involves females and immature males.

Eider *(Somateria mollissima)*   *Resident and winter visitor*
The first breeding record of Eider in Cumbria occurred on Walney Island in 1949. Since then the success of the bird in the Walney/Foulney area has been increasing annually. During 1983, *five thousand* birds were counted at the Walney Bird Observatory on 13 Feb, with *five hundred and fifty* nests found in May. During the winter months birds from this population are now being found in the Duddon and around Morecambe Bay as far as the Leven Estuary. Elsewhere along the Cumbrian coast the bird is an irregular visitor.

It is rare inland, so a previously unpublished record of a female on Killington Reservoir on 24 Nov, 1944 (Sedgwick Society, Sedbergh School) is noteworthy.

King Eider *(Somateria spectabilis)*   *Vagrant*
A drake was seen at Walney Bird Observatory with Eiders on 10-23 Jun, 1979 and again 12 Apr-1 May, 1980. This bird was seen by many observers and was the first and second records for North-west England and the county.

Long-tailed Duck *(Clangula hyemalis)* *Irregular winter visitor*
This duck is a regular but uncommon winter visitor occurring in *ones* and *twos* on the Solway, around Walney Island and in Morecambe Bay. Inland it is irregular, being found infrequently on the larger lakes like Windermere. *Five,* 7-13 Nov, 1976 on Killington Reservoir was unusual.

Most records involve females and immature males.

Common Scoter *(Melanitta nigra)*   *Passage migrant*

Although the Common Scoter is a non-breeding visitor to Cumbria, it has been recorded in every month of the year. It is a frequent bird along the coast, sometimes gathering into very large flocks. *c one thousand, seven hundred and fifty,* 2 May, 1965 off Foulney Island and *c one thousand five hundred,* 16 Dec, 1979 off Silecroft being recent examples of this.

Inland the bird is irregular although in recent years it has been recorded almost annually well away from the coast, particularly in the summer months. *Single* birds are usually recorded although *four,* 5 May, 1978 were at Pull Wyke Bay, Lake Windermere and *two,* 2 Jul, 1978 were on Killington Reservoir. Single birds are fairly regularly recorded each year at this latter site, giving rise to speculation that a cross country migration from east to west may be taking place. Larger flocks inland are rare, even though Stokoe mentions *fifty* birds being recorded on Ullswater in July. It was very unusual then for *fifty-two* birds to be found roosting on Haweswater, 13 Oct, 1983, by Miss K M Atkinson during a wildfowl count.

Surf Scoter *(Melanitta perspicillata)*   *Vagrant*

Stokoe BLC records an old record 'near Carlisle, Nov 1856'. This rarity has been recorded several times near the Scottish shore of the Solway in the period covered.

Velvet Scoter *(Melanitta fusca)*   *Irregular winter visitor*

This is an irregular visitor to the Cumbrian coastline, appearing usually between August and May. They appear in *ones* and *twos,* often in flocks of Common Scoters.

A drake which was first seen at the Walney Bird Observatory in the winter 1980/81, became a resident at the reserve. It could be seen regularly in the Walney channel and was still present in Nov, 1984, although it was absent during the summer months of 1984.

Away from the coast the bird is rare, although Stokoe BLC mentions that it has been recorded on Lake Windermere. Two records away from the coast during the period include a drake on Killington Reservoir, 6 Dec, 1978 (A F Gould) and a duck on the River Esk on Rockcliffe Marsh, 22-27 Feb, 1981 (R Armstrong).

Goldeneye *(Bucephala clangula)*   *Winter visitor*

This is a common winter visitor which appears from October to April. Birds frequent most lakes, rivers and estuaries, being less common on the sea. Females outnumber the males during the winter, but migrant breeding and non-breeding males join them in March when flocks of *thirty* birds and over are often recorded.

In the last ten years or so, summering birds have been recorded on some of the larger lakes, giving rise to speculation that it may become a possible breeding bird in the county in the future.

Smew *(Mergus albellus)*   *Irregular winter visitor*
An annual but scarce winter visitor to the county, the Smew occurs between November and March. It frequents lakes, reservoirs, rivers and estuaries where usually *single* birds are involved. Numbers increase in periods of hard weather conditions when many birds move westwards from the continent. It is unusual to record more than *five* birds together in the county, so *eight,* 5 Mar, 1954 at Rusland Pool (A F Airey) and *seven,* 17 Feb, 1963 on Cavendish Dock, Barrow (R S Wimpress) are noteworthy.

Red-breasted Merganser *(Mergus serrator)* *Breeding resident and passage bird*
Reference to the spread throughout the county of this bird as a breeding resident can be found in Stokoe BLC. Since the first breeding record on the River Esk in 1950 it has spread to most lakes, rivers and tarns in the county, although it is less common as a breeding bird on the coast, except in the Foulney/Walney area.

Up to *two hundred and fifty* birds gather in July in the Hodbarrow area on the Duddon to moult. But recent commercial development at this site has dispersed the birds further down the estuary.

Numbers of winter migrants occur from the estuaries of Morecambe Bay round the coast to the Solway. Usually flocks of up to *fifty* birds are recorded, but in favoured localities like Ravenglass area, the Duddon estuary, around Walney and Cavendish Dock flocks of a *hundred* birds plus have been recorded in severe conditions.

Goosander *(Mergus merganser)* *Breeding resident and winter visitor*
Like the Red-breasted Merganser, this duck first bred in the county in 1950. Stokoe BLC refers to it as spreading slowly in the northern half of the county. Over the last twenty years the

bird has spread through the central region to the southern estuaries of Morecambe Bay. Although it has not increased as rapidly as the Red-breasted Merganser, it now breeds in small numbers on some of the central lakes and on the rivers Lune, Kent and Leven.

Winter visitors are variable in numbers according to the severity of the weather conditions. It is a common bird on the larger lakes, rivers and tarns up to 1,800 ft., where up to *sixty* birds can occur. 'Red-heads' outnumber adult males, *one hundred and sixteen,* 26 Jan, 1964 on Killington Reservoir being an exceptionally large gathering. It is uncommon on the coast.

Ruddy Duck *(Oxyura jamaicensis)*

A North American species introduced into Britain at Slimbridge, Gloucestershire in 1948. It is thought that up to *seventy* juveniles flew away from the Wildfowl Trust between 1956 and 1963 forming a feral population in the Midlands and South-West of England.

It was admitted to the official British and Irish list as recently as 1971. The following are the first records for the county;

> *Female,* 27 Aug, 1980, Longtown gravel pits (R Armstrong, M Ramsden).
> *Two males and three females,* 2 May, 1981, Standing Tarn, Dalton-in-Furness (C Raven).
> *Female,* 21 Dec, 1981, Cavendish Dock Barrow (T Dean)
> *Immature male,* 5-10 Jan, 1982, Hodbarrow (D B Thexton, T Dean *et al*)
> *Male,* 1 and 24 Apr, 1983, Cavendish Dock (L H Sanderson).

Honey Buzzard *(Pernis apivorus)*   *Very rare migrant*

Stokoe BLC records the last record as being in 1925. It has not been recorded in the last twenty years since his publication.

Red Kite *(Milvus milvus)*   *Rare migrant*

As with most of England this bird was a former resident. Stokoe's BLC states the last known record as being at Workington in June, 1921. Since that work, there has been a fair sprinkling of records over the last twenty years. The most notable of these was a bird which wintered for two seasons in the Ravenstonedale Moor area during 1976/77 and 1977/78. The other records are;

Immature, 22 Oct, 1974, Bannisdale (A F Gould).
Adult, 5 Aug, 1978, Bootle (A B Warburton)
Adult, 29 May, 1979, High Hesket, seen flying south (B Hardcastle).
Adult, 31 Dec, 1980, Culgaith (G Horne).
The only other record is of a Kite of unidentified species seen over St Bees Head on 10 Apr, 1970 (*per* R Stokoe).

White-tailed Eagle *(Haliaeetus albicilla)*   *Vagrant*
Stokoe's BLC refers to this former resident as last being seen in March 1934 over Coniston Water.

Marsh Harrier *(Circus aeruginosus)*   *Rare migrant*
The Marsh Harrier bred in the county in the nineteenth century but now has become a rare passage migrant. Most records come from the coast, particularly Walney Bird Observatory, where *fifteen* out of *eighteen* coastal migrants have been recorded in the last twenty years. Sightings elsewhere include;
    Immature/female, 21 May, 1969, Heversham Moss (Arnside NHS).
    Pair, 10-15 May, 1975, Hutton-in-the-Forest (R W Robson).
    Female, 24th May, 1979, Sunbiggin Tarn (A A & M Hutcheson)
    Male, 15 Apr, 1981, Selside, near Kendal (S J Dodgson).
    Immature Male, 15 Jun, 1982, Newbiggin/Cumrew area (J Miles).

Hen Harrier *(Circus cyaneus)*   *Passage migrant*
Although the Hen harrier has increased its range in Northern Britain, it still remains an irregular visitor to the county. Breeding records over the period have been very sporadic and scattered over the region with the most sights being in the Northern Pennines. At least *one pair* successfully bred in the Lake District area in 1978, which unfortunately is not a regular occurrence.

It is most frequently seen as a winter visitor between the months of October and March, when it can be found on coastal saltmarshes and mosses as well as at a higher altitude in the Central Fells and other open country.

Hen Harrier.

Montagu's Harrier *(Circus pygargus)*   *Rare passage migrant*
This Harrier has become a rarity in recent years with only a *few pairs* breeding each year in Southern Britain. The following three records are the first since the last breeding attempt in the old county of Cumberland in 1923.

> *Male,* 7 Oct, 1961, Meaburn Edge, Maulds Meaburn (N P & H Morgan; Field Nat: Vol 6, No 6).
> *Male,* 4 Apr, 1978, Claife Heights, Windermere (B H Lee, R Freethy).
> *Male,* 20 Apr, 1981, Walney Bird Observatory (T Dean).

Goshawk *(Accipiter gentilis)*   *Irregular migrant*
Records of this raptor have been increasing annually over the period in suitable habitat up to the current situation where the *odd pair* has remained in an area in the breeding season. The first recorded positive breeding success came in 1983 when a *pair* raised *two* young.

Most records come in the Autumn when *single* birds have been seen in wide range of forestry type situations.

Sparrowhawk *(Accipiter nisus)*   *Resident and passage migrant*
The Sparrowhawk is a fairly regular sight throughout the county. Its numbers have remained almost static for many years when in other parts of the country its numbers have fluctuated.

Between September and April there is an increase in numbers at coastal and estuarine sites. Whether this is a movement of passage migrants or just the resident population moving down to the lower levels from fellside habitat remains unproven.

A bird was seen on 2 June, 1982 in Holker Park, Cartmel, carrying a Grass Snake. There is no mention of this as being a food item in "Birds of the Western Palearctic" (Cramp & Simmons).

Buzzard *(Buteo buteo)* *Resident*

During the last twenty years the range of the Buzzard has increased, particularly in the south of the county where it is now a regular sight as far as the Lancashire and Yorkshire borders. Even in the Solway Plain in the north it is becoming a more regular visitor, this being the area where it was never a common bird.

Nest sites are generally in trees and on crags on the fells, often up to the two thousand foot level in the Pennines.

In quiet spells of weather, small family groups can often be seen soaring together, but *twenty-one* in view over Grizedale on 28 Oct, 1973 (R Freethy) was unusual.

Rough-legged Buzzard *(Buteo lagopus)* *Irregular winter visitor*

This raptor usually appears from November to March and could easily be overlooked in an area where the Buzzard is common, It occurs more frequently in eastern Britain so the seven records received in the last twenty years are noteworthy.

One, 28 Mar, 1965, Burnmoor Tarn.

One, 8 Mar, 1966, Potter Fell, Longsleddale (J A G Barnes).

One, 15 Sep, 1974, Kentmere (J Driver).

One, 10 Feb, 1979, Kentmere (C Lythgoe).

One, 21 Sep, 1979, Eskdale (A B Warburton)

One, 30 Dec, 1979, Smardale Gill (R & D Baines)

One, 27 Jan-30 Mar, 1980, Ash Fell, Kirkby Stephen (R & D Baines)

Golden Eagle *(Aquila chrysaetos)* *Scarce breeding resident*

The success of breeding Eagles in the county has been a well published event. A breeding *pair* were successful in rearing *one* youngster in 1969, this was the first reared eagle in England for nearly 200 years. A *second pair* of birds were successful in rearing a youngster in 1976 and since that date success rate has been varied with no young being reared in 1981. Weather conditions and disturbance are the main features controlling their success rate.

Three birds have been found dead since 1976, including *one* of the breeding males which was in the summer of 1976. The female found a replacement mate by the next season.

It must be said that but for the sterling work put in annually by a small band of conservationists of the RSPB, Nature Conservancy and other involved organisations, eagles would not be in the Lake District at the present time. It is hoped that hopeful 'eagle-watchers' reading this and visiting the Lake District will do so outside the breeding season as the birds are great wanderers, particularly the immature birds.

Birds seen in the county before 1969 probably came from Southern Scotland. Two notable records include a bird watched all day on 8th June 1958 in the Witherslack/ Whitbarrow Scar area by fifteen members of the Fylde Naturalists Society. Another bird was seen over Nibthwaite, near Ulverston on 26 Mar, 1963.

Osprey *(Pandion haliaetus)*   *Irregular passage migrant*
Once a former breeding bird, the Osprey is now a scarce migrant visitor in the county. Immature birds have lingered in some areas during the summer months, but most records come during Spring and Autumn migration. A bird at Bolton Mill, near Appleby on 29 Mar, 1974 and another over Derwentwater on 3 Mar, 1978 were early dates. A bird seen by J W Allen in Kentmere on 9 Nov, 1979 was a late date.

Kestrel *(Falco tinnunculus)*   *Resident and passage migrant*
This is the most successful bird of prey in the county being relatively common in all areas except those of open agriculture. It frequents railway embankments, farmland with mixed woodland, coastal mosses, upland sites in the Lake District mountains and in the Pennines as well as urban sites in towns and villages. It has adapted to the new environment of a modern motorway system, where birds can be seen hunting the large embankments along the road network.

It is often not considered as a migrant bird, but numbers do increase in Spring and especially in the Autumn. As many as *six* birds can be found together during August—October at the Walney Bird Observatory during a season of normal migration.

Ringing also proves the bird to be a traveller from as far afield as the continent, examples being a bird ringed at Brough on 11 Jun, 1968, which was shot near Le Brieue, Cotes du Nord, France on 16 Nov, 1969. Another bird ringed at

Appleby on 8 Jul, 1979 was found dead at Borkum, West Germany on 10 Sep, 1980, a distance of 608 km.

Red-footed Falcon *(Falco vespertinus)* *Vagrant*
Stokoe BLC records two old records, both males at Lowther in 1929 and at Alston in 1932.

Merlin *(Falco columbarius)* *Breeding visitor & passage migrant*
The Merlin has declined very significantly in the last twenty years, so that the bird's status in the county can be regarded now as uncommon.

It still breeds sporadically in the Pennines, as well as the Southern and Central Fells. Its nest site is usually a heather clad hillside, but it is also known to nest on crags and in trees.

It frequents lowland areas and the coast in the winter months. Passage migrants also occur around the coast during Spring and Autumn, often following migrating flocks of waders and passerines. A male watched at Bootle by A B Warburton on 15 Nov, 1982 was killed chasing a Starling through a farmhouse window, and was found to be ringed at Reykjavik, Iceland.

Hobby *(Falco subbuteo)* *Rare passage migrant*
Stokoe BLC records this bird as a breeding visitor in the early part of the century. During the period it is recorded as a scarce migrant.

One, 27 Jul, 1979, Askam, Penrith *(per* R Stokoe).

Male, 4 May, 1981, Foulney Island and Walney Bird Observatory (A Phizacklea, T Dean).

Male, 28 Aug-1 Sep, 1981, Barrow-in-Furness, seen to catch a House Martin (J Sheldon).

One, 26 Jun, 1982, Whitbarrow Scar (T H Jorgensen).

One, 12 Oct, 1982, Grange-over-Sands (F C Dawson).

One, 23 Oct, 1982, Whitehaven (R S Wimpress).

One, 2 May, 1983, Houghton, Carlisle (R Armstrong).

One, 28 May, 1984, Davenby Craggs, Cockermouth (K Dorman).

One, 4-7 Oct, 1984, Walney Island (T Dean, J & J Sheldon).

Gyrfalcon *(Falco rusticolus)* *Vagrant*
Stokoe BLC gives an account of seven old records. Two more recent records are;

Adult, 16 Dec, 1961, Duddon Estuary (F J Ellwood, K J St Ruth) (Field Nat: Vol 6, No 2)
Juvenile, 17-18 Dec, 1983, Rampside, Barrow-in-Furness (T Dean, S Lawson, L H Sanderson *et al*).

Peregrine *(Falco peregrinus)*   *Resident and passage migrant*
Cumbria is the main inland stronghold of the Peregrine in England. As occurred elsewhere, the Cumbrian population suffered a dramatic decline in the late 1950's and 1960's due to the effect of pesticides poisoning. by 1963 there were just eight territories occupied, *four pairs* producing eggs and *two* broods reared. Numbers remained at this dismal level until 1967 when the recovery began, continuing up to 1979 when there were at least thirty-three territories in the Lake District ('The Peregrine Falcon', D A Ratcliffe).

The 1981 Peregrine Falcon survey revealed a continuing increase which by 1982 had reached a level which was close to the highest breeding density recorded for inland nesting Peregrines anywhere in the world. This was higher than for any previous occasion for inland Britain.

This increase has involved the occupation of new nesting cliffs, the regular use of previously irrregularly used cliffs and the doubling up within previously single territories (Bird Study; vol 31-1). This success has been achieved in spite of continuing persecution by egg-collectors and so-called 'falconers' and the like.

Some *pairs* remain in their breeding territories throughout the winter, whilst other sites are occupied by *one* bird or deserted altogether. Peregrines are frequently sighted on the coast and estuaries during the winter, most birds being immatures. In this respect a bird ringed as an eyass on a Lake District breeding crag in 1982 was recovered injured after flying into a fence on the Ribble Marshes, Lancashire during February 1983. This gives some clue to the movement in winter of locally bred birds. It is also recorded in well populated areas at this time, an example being a bird which used the shipyard cranes in Vickers Shipyard, Barrow-in-Furness, as a regular roost and vantage point during the winter of 1978.

The much larger Scandinavian race *(F. p. calidus)* was recorded at Walney Bird Observatory during October and December 1980.

Red Grouse *(Lagopus lagopus scoticus)* *Resident*

A fairly common game-bird on the heather moorland of the Pennines and the eastern Central Fells. Rather thinly distributed elsewhere and all but disappeared from the coastal mosses.

Ptarmigan *(Lagopus mutus)*

Extinct since the Eighteenth century.

Black Grouse *(Tetrao tetrix)* *Resident*

Still fairly common on the moors of the Northern Pennines. Elsewhere local populations are scattered where the combination of heather and woodland cover is available. Numbers vary with the changes in the use of the ground they occupy, the activities of the forestry industry being important in this respect.

No records have come from the southern mosses or limestone uplands during the period, where they were once regular. One can only assume they are restricted to remaining suitable habitat in the Furness and Shap Fells.

Capercaillie *(Tetrao urogallus)*

A scheme where *several pairs* of Capercaillie were introduced into Grizedale Forest in 1972, seems to have dwindled away into extinction as no records have been recorded over the last ten years.

Red-legged Partridge *(Alectoris rufa)* *Introduction*

Several introductions of this game-bird have been made by various shooting syndicates in the last twenty years. *One or two* small populations can be found in the Derwent, Eden and Kent valleys. Stragglers are often found many miles away from the site of introduction.

Grey Partridge *(Perdix perdix)* *Resident*

The Grey Partridge has declined in the county in the last twenty years. It is still common in arable areas, but less numerous on grazing land and infrequent on fellsides and higher ground, up to 1,000 ft.

Winter coveys of around 15 birds are normal, so a covey of forty-one birds seen on 24 Dec, 1982 on North Walney was noteworthy.

Quail *(Coturnix coturnix)*   *Irregular summer migrant*

This scarce summer visitor has become less frequent in the period under review, with only sixteen records in the last twenty years. It has been found more often on land near the coast and in the Solway Plain.

Breeding records during this time are restricted to a *pair* with a clutch of eggs being found at Dearham, July 1969 (Miss M M Milne).

Pheasant *(Phasianus colchicus)*   *Resident*

Particularly common where they are bred and released for game-shooting, but tend to be scarce elsewhere. Melanistic, albino and other colour forms are occasionally seen.

Water Rail *(Rallus aquaticus)*   *Resident*

This bird is more often noticed during the winter months when they are occasionally seen in hard conditions, sometimes in unusual situations. It is often recognised in Spring by its pig-like squealing as it defends its territory.

The breeding population in the country is rather restricted as the bird prefers lakes, tarns, reservoirs and gravel pits where there is ample reed cover.

It is a migratory bird in small numbers in the county, an example of this being a bird ringed on 2 Jul, 1966 at Niedersachsen, W. Germany which was recovered at Piel Island, Barrow-in-Furness on 4 Apr, 1970, a distance of 800 kms.

Spotted Crake *(Porzana porzana)*   *Rare migrant*

This is an irregular and scarce summer visitor to the county. records for the period under review are;

One, 7 Oct, 1962, Longnewton Marsh (W D Slater)

One, 8-12 Jun, 1964, New Hall, Appleby (R W Robson).

One, 21 Jul, 1970, Potter Fell Dubs (A Whiteside, J W Allen).

One, 12-27 Aug with *three,* 27 Aug, 1981, Scaleby Moss (R Armstrong, M Ramsden).

One, 5 Oct, 1981, North Walney (L H Sanderson).

One, 26 Sep, 1983, Walney Bird Observatory (L H Sanderson).

Little Crake *(Porzana parva)*   *Vagrant*

Stokoe's BLC refers to three records; *one,* 1850 shot near Cockermouth Castle; *one,* 19 Apr, 1886, Ulverston and *one,* Nov, 1940, at Dalston.

During the period under review just one additional record has come to light;

> One, 16-19 Jul, 1965, Ratherheath Tarn, near Kendal (J W Allen, A Whiteside).

This bird was both seen and heard by both observers (Field Naturalist: Vol 10, No 3).

Baillon's Crake *(Porzana pusilla)*   *Vagrant*

Stokoe's BLC refers to an old record at Ulverston, May 1886.

Corncrake *(Crex crex)*   *Irregular summer visitor*

It is an unfortunate fact, that the Corncrake has become an uncommon migrant in the county over the last twenty years, in common with its general demise elsewhere in the country.

Most records in Cumbria come from areas near the coast and in the Solway Plain and usually involve passage migrants. Breeding records are sporadic. The last positive record involved *a pair* in the Lyth Valley, near Brigsteer in 1971 (F Barker, J Robinson).

Moorhen *(Gallinula chloropus)*   *Resident*

A common bird in suitable waterside habitat by open water from the smallest pond to the largest lakes and reservoirs. It is also found by rivers, streams, canals and ditches.

Numbers have dropped in some areas due to predation by Mink.

Coot *(Fulica atra)*   *Resident and passage migrant*

The Coot favours the larger lakes and tarns which have Willows and/or reeds on their fringe, to give the birds cover and a breeding site.

Numbers increase during the Autumn and Winter on the larger lakes and lowland tarns as the local population is increased by birds coming from upland waters and migrants.

Some high totals have come from the larger waters of the county with *c one thousand, one hundred and two,* 4 Oct, 1979 on Bassenthwaite Water, *c one thousand, two hundred and forty,* 11 Jan, 1979, Lake Windermere and *c six hundred and twenty-five,* 23 Oct, 1982 on Cavendish Dock.

The Coot is rarely seen on salt water except in conditions of severe frost.

Crane *(Grus grus)*   *Vagrant*

Stokoe's BLC records an old record at Allonby, 1869. Other records in the period include a flock of *twelve,* flying west,

23 Sep, 1954, over Brampton (H R Nicholl).
> *One,* 30 Sep, 1979, to 6 Jan, 1980, Flookburgh Marshes (V P W Lowe, B B Wilson).
> *One,* 5 Oct, 1984, Walney Bird Observatory (J Robinson-Dean, T Dean)

Demoiselle Crane *(Anthropoides virgo)*   *Vagrant*
A Demoiselle Crane, identified as an immature bird, was present on the Upper Kent Estuary from 6-21 Sep, 1967. Although the bird was remarkably wary it was not accepted by BBRC, as it was at that time regarded to be an escapee, thus the record remains underlined (J W Allen, J Wilson, R S Wimpress).

Great Bustard *(Otis tarda)*   *Vagrant*
Stokoe's BLC records an old record at Lanercost, March 1854.

Oystercatcher *(Haematopus ostralegus)*   *Resident and passage migrant*
Since the Oystercatcher has developed the habit of moving inland to breed in Northern Britain, it has now become one of our most common waders.

It nests on shingle bank situations on the coast or on our larger river systems, with smaller numbers nesting on estuarine saltmarshes.

When the breeding season is complete, family groups gather in large numbers with many incoming migrants on the cockle and mussel beds of Morecambe Bay and the Solway. Examples of maximum totals at this time are *c ten thousand,* 20 Aug, 1979 on Foulney Island and *c twenty-four thousand, eight hundred,* 28 Sep, 1980 at Cardurnock.

The Morecambe Bay Wader Group have ringed and studied the movements of Oystercatchers and have found them fairly sedentary with the more distant recoveries coming from Denmark, Norway, Iceland and the Faroes. A bird ringed on Walney Island, 19 Jan, 1969 was recovered dead, 11 Jun, 1977 on Bear Island, Spitzbergen, several hundred miles north of the top of Norway. This was the most northerly ever recovered by the British Ringing Scheme.

Avocet *(Recurvirostra avosetta)*   *Rare passage migrant*
One found in the mouth of a stream at Oldkiln, Allonby on 17 Dec, 1963, is an odd winter migrant, not previously recorded. Other records in the period include a bird which

was seen in several parts of Morecambe Bay throughout the summer of 1981.

One, 3-5 Oct, 1970, Upper Kent Estuary (J A G Barnes).

One, 15 May, 1981, Talkin Tarn (J Miles).

One, 16 May, 1981, Priory Point, Bardsea (J Wilson).

One, 19 May, 1981, Meathop (J A G Barnes).

One, 5 Jul, 1981, Canal Foot, South Ulverston (S C Peter).

One, 6 Sep, 1981, Low Foulshaw, Upper Kent Estuary (M Hutcheson).

One, 1-4 Jun, 1983, Grisedale, Garsdale (E H Warmington, J & M Banks *et al*).

Stone Curlew *(Burhinus oedicnemus)*   *Rare summer visitor*
Stokoe's BLC mentions four records for the county. A bird was found in a field with Lapwing near Old Park Wood, Holker, Cartmel, 29 Aug, 1976 (F Tinker).

Cream-coloured Courser *(Cursorius cursor)*   *Vagrant*
Stokoe's BLC refers to two old records. One shot at Allonby, Oct, 1862 and a male shot at Grune Point, Solway, by John Stockdale, 15 Oct, 1947, which is now in the Tullie House Museum, Carlisle.

Collared Pratincole *(Glareola pratincola)*   *Vagrant*
An old Solway record in 1807. A bird was seen flying low past Priest Island, on Leven Estuary, 19 Aug, 1973, by members of the Morecambe Bay Wader Group. The exact identity whether it was a bird of the red or black-winged race could not be determined (Dr C Clapham, J Sheldon *et al*). Record was accepted by the BBRC (BB Vol 66, No 11).

Little Ringed Plover *(Charadrius dubius)*   *Scarce summer migrant*
Up to 1970, the Little Ringed Plover was considered a rare bird in Cumbria. Since that date it has occurred nine times throughout the county, mainly immatures in Autumn.

The first breeding record came in 1970 when *a pair* reared *four* young on a shingle bank on the River Eden. During the drought of 1984, two pairs were successful in rearing at least *seven* young on the dried out bed of Killington Reservoir.

Ringed Plover *(Charadrius hiaticula)*   *Resident and passage migrant*
This attractive wader is being seen more often inland on favoured rivers, tarns and reservoirs. Some breeding records also come from these sites, but the bird is normally associated

with our coasts and estuaries where it nests on shingle and sand-banks near the high water line.

Although present in small numbers throughout the year, large flocks accumulate in May and September during the migration period around the coastline. These flocks often reach *several hundreds* in numbers.

It is a well travelled migrant, the MBWG having had ringing recoveries from six European countries as well as Morocco, Norway, Iceland and Greenland.

A notable record is of a bird ringed 30 Apr, 1971, Bardsea, found dead, 4 Jul, 1978 at Godthaab, Greenland.

Dotterel *(Charadrius morinellus) Irregular passage and breeding visitor*

As a breeding bird, the Dotterel has a very precarious foothold in Cumbria. *One or two pairs* attempt to breed each year, but are not always successful in rearing young due to various pressures on the fell tops, particularly by disturbance and weather conditions.

They occur on the higher Lakeland mountains and the Pennines in May during migration, in small parties or 'trips', often at recognised gathering points. During the return Autumn migration birds are occasionally found at lower levels and around the coast, being recorded well into October.

Golden Plover *(Pluvialis apricaria) Resident and passage migrant*

The Golden Plover is a regular breeding bird in the Pennines and is fairly common on moorland above 1,000 ft. Elsewhere in the Lakeland Fells it is not so common with breeding only taking place in a few favoured areas. They are present in their breeding haunts from March until August.

During the autumn the birds form post-breeding flocks using regular inland sites of open grassland, often near an upland tarn or river. These flocks then move to their coastal wintering grounds. Large open spaces in an estuarine or coastal location are chosen, in particular old airfields, golf courses and large areas of saltmarsh grassland.

The boldly marked northern race *(P. apricaria altifrons)* can be found in varying numbers amongst Spring and Autumn passage flocks. A bird of this northern race was found occupying a nest-site in the Pennines in June 1979 with a mate of the local race.

Ringing has proved the Golden Plover to travel well into Southern Europe during migration, with records coming

Paddyfield Warbler —
Walney Bird Observatory, 11th September, 1982
Photos: D. Satterthwaite

Bee-eater — *Sizergh Castle, 8th June, 1981*

Little Owl — *New Hutton, 29th June, 1975*

Tawny Owl (Rufous phase) on nest in old Crow's nest — *Bannisdale, 4th May, 1976*

Little Ringed Plover (Immature) — *Killington Reservoir, 1st August., 1984*

Knot — *Kirksanton, 5th May, 1985*

Spotted Redshank — *Fisher Tarn, 27th August, 1967*

Raven — *Borrowdale, Shap, 17th December, 1978*

Buzzard — *Forest Hall, Selside, 25th January, 1981*

Arctic Skua (Immature) — *Burneside Hall, 6th October, 1976*

Oystercatcher — *Killington Reservoir, 9th May, 1978*

Common Snipe with young — *Lambrigg Fell, 26th June, 1980*

Moorhen — *Kendal Sewage Works, 30 April, 1976*

Long-tailed Tit — *Gurnal Bridge, Selside, 10th May, 1977*

Reed Warbler at nest — *Esthwaite Water, 8th July, 1980*

Sand Martin — *Levens Park, 11th July, 1978*

Redpoll — *Bannisdale, 13th July, 1979*

Great Grey Shrike — *Sizergh, 20th March, 1983*

Ring Ousel (female) — *Bannisdale, 31st October, 1976*

Yellowhammer — *Bannisdale, 2nd July, 1979*

Dotterel (Passage birds) — *Pennines, 24th May, 1978*

Wheatear (male) — *Bannisdale, 6th June, 1976*

Yellow-browed Warbler — *Walney Bird Observatory, 26th September, 1985*
Photographed by D. Satterthwaite

from as far as Spain and Italy. A local recovery of a bird ringed 1 Jun, 1978 at Kirkby Stephen being found shot 17 Jan, 1980 at St Vivian, Gironde, France (1008 km.) is typical of this southern movement.

Grey Plover *(Pluvialis squatarola)*   *Winter visitor and passage migrant*

This bird is a regular winter visitor to the Solway and the Walney/Foulney area. It is less common on the Cumbrian coast and the Morecambe Bay estuaries, though they do occur here regularly in small numbers. Passage birds add to the local winter populations in Spring and Autumn, particularly in May and September. Peak figures in recent years include;

> *Five hundred and four,* 14 Feb, 1983, Cardurnock, Solway.
> *One hundred and twenty-four,* 18 Dec, 1983, Walney Bird Observatory.
> *Eighty-four,* 19 Dec, 1984, Flookburgh Marshes.

It is rare inland, but has been known to occur, usually singly, with Golden Plover flocks. Inland records for the period include; a bird flying west, 26 Nov, 1976 at Sunbiggin Tarn (R & D Barnes), and another bird seen flying west, 14 Sep, 1978, over the summit of Froswick, Kentmere (E & R Parkes).

Lapwing *(Vanellus vanellus)*   *Resident and passage migrant*

The Lapwing is a regular breeding bird from the coastline to the 2,000 ft. level in the Pennines and Lakeland mountains.

Post-breeding flocks gather on the estuaries of the county, with peak numbers being recorded in the early part of the Autumn. During this time an average of *four thousand* birds can be found on the Solway and on the Kent Estuary on Morecambe Bay. During severe conditions in the winter passage birds move in from the Continent often giving larger totals than this peak figure. Numbers are often variable through the winter as birds come into the region and move on south-westwards. The MBWG have had recoveries from as far south as France and Spain and west into Ireland. A local recovery in this pattern was a bird ringed 1 Jun, 1971 at Shap, which was found dead on 23 Jan, 1972 in Orthez (Pyrenees Atlantique), France.

Knot *(Calidris canutus)*   *Winter visitor and passage migrant*

The Estuaries of North West England are vitally important as a feeding ground to the Knot, on its migration to Greenland and the Arctic where they breed.

By far the most favoured area for this bird to spend the winter months is Morecambe Bay, with an average of *thirty-four thousand* birds being recorded over the last ten years. The Duddon and the Solway are also important to the Knot, with numbers at all three sites coming to a peak during the Spring when passage birds add to the wintering birds. MBWG have had recoveries of Knot from five European countries as well as Iceland, Greenland and Spain.

Inland records of this bird are unusual, so a bird in summer plumage on 30 Jul, 1978 at Killington Reservoir (R I Kinley), is noteworthy.

Sanderling *(Calidris alba)*   *Winter visitor and passage migrant*
This wader favours large areas of sand and can be found on all the county's estuaries in this type of habitat. Peak figures occur in Spring, when the birds in summer plumage become inconspicuous from its near relative, the Dunlin which has a similar plumage.

MBWG have had recoveries of this wader in Europe and East Germany. An interesting recovery is of a bird ringed 8 May, 1980 at Biggar, Walney being found dead, 1 Mar, 1981, at Safi, Morocco.

Inland records are unusual with *three* birds, 8 Mar, 1976 at Glenridding, Ullswater and a spate in 1982 with *singles* at Killington Reservoir, 15 May; Wet Sleddale Dam, 16 May and Sunbiggin Tarn on 6 Aug. In 1983 a *single* bird appeared at Wet Sleddale Dam on 7 Aug with *four* at Sunbiggin Tarn on the same day.

Little Stint *(Calidris minuta)*   *Autumn passage migrant*
This bird appears in small numbers each Autumn in estuarine habitat. Usually birds appear in *ones and twos* with *fifteen,* 24 Sep, 1983 on the Upper Kent Estuary being exceptional.

Stokoe's BLC records birds over-wintering in the county and during the period under review a bird was found on 12 Jan, 1977 at Walney Bird Observatory with others during 1983 at Sandside, Furness on 10 Feb and Esk Estuary on 13 Feb (C Isherwood, M Madders).

Spring records are also unusual with a bird on 24/25 May, 1978 at Arnside Marsh (J A G Barnes); *two,* 30 Apr, 1982, Walney Bird Observatory; *three,* 15 May, 1982, Dubmill Point, Allonby (J C Callion); *one,* 15 Apr, 1983, Siddick Pond, Workington (J C Callion).

Inland records are not common, unlike other areas in the country. Killington Reservoir had *single* birds during drought conditions on 2 Aug to 29 Sep, 1976 and 27 Aug, 1982.

Temminck's Stint *(Calidris temminckii)*   *Rare passage bird*
Stokoe's BLC records six old occurrences of this bird, all of them in September. Spring records are unusual in Britain, so *three* birds found in June 1963 and *one* in May 1979 are exceptional. Records for the period are;

One, 15 Sep, 1962, Foulney Island (B G Sutton).
Three, 3 Jun, 1963, Roosecote Marsh, Barrow (M Jones, J H Morgan, G Blackwell).
One, 17 May, 1979, Hodbarrow (D B Thexton).
One, 6 Sep, 1983, Walney Bird Observatory (T Dean).

White-rumped Sandpiper *(Calidris fuscicollis)*   *Vagrant*
A record of this North American vagrant found on the coast at Seascale, 3 Oct, 1959, is given in full detail in The Field Naturalist, Vol 4, No 6 (D S Sodo). This record has not been submitted to the BBRC.

One, 1-2 Aug, 1984, Hodbarrow (D B Thexton, R I Kinley *et al*)
One, 13 Oct, 1984, Walney Bird Observatory (J V Bhalerao, J R C Dakin *et al*)
Both these records were accepted by the BBRC. Both birds were adults.

Baird's Sandpiper *(Calidris bairdii)*   *Vagrant*
A bird found and identified on Arnside Marsh, Kent Estuary from 24 to 30 Sep, 1979, was one of nine records in Britain of this American wader during that year (J C Gregory, P J Marsh, J A Wolstencroft). The record was accepted by BBRC. This is the only record for Cumbria.

Pectoral Sandpiper *(Calidris melanotos)*   *Rare passage bird*
This American wader was removed from the BBRC rarity list in 1983 due to its annual appearance in Britain in recent years. Stokoe's BLC refers to two old records. Other records in the period are;

One, 11-12 Jun, 1963, Roosecote Marsh (B G Sutton, W H Tickle, K Brown).
One, 31 Jul-3 Aug, 1982, Walney Bird Observatory (T Dean, D Satterthwaite).
One, 28-30 Aug, 1984, Meathop, Kent Estuary (R I Kinley, P Robinson *et al*)

Curlew Sandpiper *(Calidris ferruginea)* *Autumn passage migrant*

Immature birds are recorded almost every year during the Autumn on all the county's estuaries, usually in small groups of under *five* birds. *Ten,* 6-7 Aug, 1978 on the Upper Kent estuary being exceptional. Spring records are very unusual and it is also scarce inland. A bird took advantage of the large area of mud on Killington Reservoir, 4-5 Sep, 1976 during the drought of that year.

Purple Sandpiper *(Calidris maritima)* *Winter visitor*

Numbers of Purple Sandpiper on the Cumbrian coast in winter are never high, as this yellow-legged, dark wader prefers a rocky coastline. Most records come from Walney Island around the Biggar Bank area where up to *forty* birds can be found most winters. A peak of *ninety-eight* was recorded here 21 Jan, 1970 but this is unusual. Elsewhere birds can be found on man-made sites like the harbours at Workington and Whitehaven.

It is rare inland, but a bird was found 30 Nov, 1976 at Windermere ferry (G Findley, J P Swales). another bird was found as far inland on a mud-bank with Dunlin, 20 Sep-11 Oct, 1981 at Foulshaw, Upper Kent estuary (A F Gould, M Hutcheson).

Dunlin *(Calidris alpina)* *Resident and passage migrant*

The Dunlin is a local breeding bird in the Pennines where its numbers seem to have decreased during the period under review. It also breeds sporadically on the estuarine saltmarshes of the Solway, Duddon and Morecambe Bay.
Large numbers congregate on the Solway and Morecambe Bay during migration and the winter months. Morecambe Bay has recorded an average of *forty-eight thousand* birds over the last eight years and is the most important site in Britain for this wader during its migration.

Smaller numbers occur elsewhere around the coast, with *one or two* birds appearing inland on lakes, tarns and reservoirs, during periods of passage.

Ringing suggests that wintering birds are from Scandinavia and Northern Russia with Spring and Autumn passage birds breeding in Iceland and wintering in Iberia. Ringing recoveries of MBWG come from eleven European countries as well as Russia, Morocco and Mauritania. Examples of this include;

A bird ringed 6 Feb, 1970 at Flookburgh, found dead 7 Sep, 1974, Yaroslavl, USSR, an inland site north-east of Moscow. A bird ringed 28 Jul, 1970 at Murmansk, USSR was recovered 19 Jan, 1977 on Walney Island and a bird ringed 12 Nov, 1973 at Serenni, Mauritania was recovered 7 May, 1978 also on Walney Island. A most peculiar recovery of a bird ringed 19 May, 1974 at Ulverston, was found 1 Jul, 1977 at Morbihan, Brittany, France in a Short-eared Owl pellet.

Buff-breasted Sandpiper *(Tryngites subruficollis)* *Vagrant*
An old Solway record of a bird shot on Burgh Marsh, September 1876 and a bird found with Dunlin, 5 Oct, 1975 on Walney Island (J Sheldon), are the only records of this American wader in Cumbria.

Ruff *(Philomachus pugnax)* *Passage migrant*
This is a regular autumn migrant in small numbers, occurring between July and September. It is usually found on salt-marshes and damp pastures on the estuaries of the region. Passage numbers of double figures are unusual but *eighteen,* 13 Jul, 1978 on the Esk Estuary, Rockcliffe; *fifteen,* 13 Sep, 1980 on a flooded field, College Green, Heversham and *fifteen,* 15 Aug, 1981 at Dubmill Point, Allonby are noteworthy.

Spring passage birds have been found on several occasions, some of which in partial summer plumage, were seen on tarns and reservoirs away from the coast.

Over-wintering has been recorded only once during the period with *nine,* 18 Feb, 1976 at Crosby-on-Eden. Winter figures have reached large numbers on the Ribble in Lancashire in recent years, so this record is not too unexpected.

Jack Snipe *(Lymnocryptes minimus)* *Passage migrant and winter visitor*
A few records of this bird are noted each year during the autumn and winter period, though nearly all records are of *single* individuals. The bird is not common and is found on mosses and moorland as well as damp places by lakes, tarns and coastal saltmarshes.

Birds are normally seen between October and April, but early records in the period were *single* birds on 6 Aug, 1977 at Fisher Tarn, Kendal and 13 Aug, 1980 at Crosby-on-Eden. A late bird was found on 5 May, 1978 on Foulney Island.

Twelve Jack Snipe were recorded shot on a rough shoot on 18 Nov, 1971 at Millom Park.

It is not often ringed by BTO ringers, so a bird ringed 15 Oct, 1966 at Walney Bird Observatory which was shot at Lanzos, Lugo, Spain on 14 Jan, 1968 made an interesting recovery.

Snipe *(Gallinago gallinago)* Resident, passage migrant and winter visitor

The Snipe is a fairly common breeding bird of wet boggy habitat frequenting areas from coastal saltmarshes to wet fellsides up to 2,500 ft.

In winter it can be found in small numbers on any wet site at lower levels and in hard conditions flocks of up to a *hundred* birds are sometimes seen. *c two hundred,* 18 Oct, 1979 found around Longtown gravel pits was exceptional.

Great Snipe *(Gallinago media)*   Vagrant

Stokoe's BLC notes thirteen records of this large snipe, the last record being a bird shot at Bampton, 26 Dec, 1963.

Dowitcher sp. *(Limnodromus sp.)*

Stokoe's BLC quotes an old record of a bird which could not be more specifically identified as a Long-billed Dowitcher or a Short-billed Dowitcher.

Woodcock *(Scolopax rusticola)* Resident, passage migrant and winter visitor

The Woodcock is locally common in open mixed woodland, especially in the south of the county. It has occasionally been found above the tree-line in the Pennines but generally is not common in open country.

It is a scarce bird on the coast, except in winter when the odd passage bird has been found. During the severe conditions of 1981/82 winter, the hard frost forced many birds to coastal sites, often in small flocks. Examples of this being *twelve,* 21 Dec, 1981 at Workington Docks and *fourteen,* 18 Dec, 1981 at Walney Bird Observatory.

Winter immigration from Northern Europe is apparent from the recovery of a bird shot 10 Jan, 1973 at Milnthorpe, as this bird was ringed 7 Nov, 1969 at Hover, Jutland in Denmark.

Black-tailed Godwit *(Limosa limosa)* Passage migrant

This is not a common bird in Cumbria, so it is interesting to note that the odd pair of birds have managed to breed on several occasions during the period on review.

Most records come with Autumn passage on the Solway and Morecambe Bay areas. Numbers rarely exceed *twenty* birds in a flock, so a flock of *c two hundred* at Walney Bird Observatory during a gale on 4 Nov, 1979 was exceptional and could possibly have involved birds of Icelandic origin. Spring and Winter records are less usual and inland records are scarce. All inland records during the period have occurred in the Spring, and are;

> *One,* 16 Apr, 1968, Ratherheath Tarn, Kendal (A Whiteside).
> *Two,* 2 May, 1979, Sunbiggin Tarn (R & D Baines).
> *Four,* 30 April, 1981, Heversham Moss (A F Gould).
> *One,* 16 May, 1982, Sunbiggin Tarn (R I Kinley, P J Robinson).

Bar-tailed Godwit *(Limosa lapponica) Winter visitor and passage migrant*

This is a common Spring and Autumn passage bird on the Cumbrian estuaries and coastline. Over the last ten years the average peak total for Morecambe Bay is *c six thousand* birds with *c four thousand* birds in the same period on the Solway. Smaller numbers are recorded throughout the winter period with immature birds often staying on during the summer. Open sandy beaches are favoured by the birds and they regularly occur between Dubmill Point and Bowness-on-Solway on the Solway and the Flookburgh Marshes in Morecambe Bay.

Inland records are infrequent, *singles* on 11-14 Sep and 5 Nov, 1976 at Killington Reservoir. A *single* flying west, 15 Sep, 1980 and *twenty-four* flying east 16 Feb, 1981 over Sizergh Castle.

Whimbrel *(Numenius phaeopus)*   *Passage migrant*

The Whimbrel is found on coastal habitat from April to October. Most birds are recorded during May, with smaller numbers being found between July and September. A few non-breeding birds are found throughout the Summer on coastal estuaries, like those around Ravenglass and on the Solway.

Large flocks have been recorded during passage movements with *c ninety,* 13 May, 1962 and *c one hundred,* 7 Aug, 1967 on South Walney. During May 1983 a heavy passage was recorded with *sixty-five,* 6 May at Kirksanton Haws, *thirty-six,* 8 May, Foulshaw, Kent Estuary; *forty,* 8 May,

Biggar, Walney and *fifty* same day at North Walney. Winter records are rare with a bird being found at the Walney Bird Observatory on 12 Feb, 1983.

Passage birds often associate with Curlew with *twenty-two* birds flying north up the Kent Estuary on 30 Apr, 1981 with *c one hundred and fifty* Curlew, being a typical example.

Some birds migrate at night, with many inland records coming from observers hearing the repetitive liquid call during the hours of darkness.

Curlew *(Numenius arquata) Breeding resident, winter visitor and passage migrant*

The Curlew is widely distributed throughout the county. Breeding birds return to their inland territories by early March. Nest-sites are chosen in open grassland on lowland farmland to moorland sites up to 2,500 ft. The birds are usually single brooded with most birds leaving their breeding sites by July, only the odd unsuccessful pair attempting a second brood and lingering sometimes into October.

Large groups of family parties gather with non-breeding birds at regular passage points during August and September, *eg* up to *six hundred* birds gather in the Sunbiggin Tarn area, before they move on to the estuaries and coast.

Morecambe Bay and the Solway are two of the most important sites for winter visitor and passage migrant birds from October to February. Morecambe Bay annually holds around *six thousand* birds at this time, while *three thousand* birds use the Solway. Many of these birds come from Scandinavia and Northern Europe and will feed and rest awhile before moving on to Southern Britain, Ireland and the Continent. MBWG have had recoveries from as far afield as Finland, France, Sweden and Germany.

Spotted Redshank *(Tringa erythropus)*   *Passage migrant*

This bird is usually found as an Autumn passage migrant occurring between July and November, although Spring and Winter records are not unknown.

It favours muddy estuarine sites and occasionally tarns and reservoirs. It has been most frequently recorded on the Solway in recent years where small flocks have occurred. *Twenty-six,* 21 Jul, 1979 at Rockcliffe Marsh and *eleven,* 9 Sep, 1980 at Grune Point being examples. During the prolonged drought conditions of 1976, many inland reservoirs dried out and Spotted Redshank were recorded at several of them including *three,* 22-27 Aug at Fisher Tarn, Kendal (A F Gould).

Other inland records for the period under review include *singles* at Ratherheath Tarn, Kendal, 15 Aug, 1969; Sunbiggin Tarn, 17 Aug, 1976 and 14-18 Aug, 1982, and Talkin Tarn on 29 Jul, 1981.

Redshank *(Tringa totanus)* *Breeding resident, winter visitor and passage migrant*

In Cumbria, this is a common bird found on rivers, estuaries and along the coastline. It breeds in damp locations from saltmarshes, dunes and coastal fields to damp moorland sites up to 1,000 ft.

Many of the Cumbrian bred birds move south in the Autumn to be replaced by birds from Northern Europe and Iceland.

During the winter it is a coastal bird with birds only moving inland during very wet weather conditions to feed in the flooded fields. During this time around *six thousand* birds are present in the Morecambe Bay area.

The ringing of Redshank on Morecambe Bay and the Solway show that it is a well travelled wader with recoveries coming from all over Europe as well as Greenland, Iceland, the Mediterranean region and North Africa.

An interesting article on the urban roosting of wintering Redshank on the River Kent in Kendal by Miss J M S Atkinson (BTO Bird Study, Vol 23, No 1, 1976) refers to Redshank roosting on buildings near the river prior to feeding on the river at dusk and often in darkness.

Greenshank *(Tringa nebularia)* *Passage migrant*

A regular Autumn migrant to our estuaries and coastline, particularly to Morecambe Bay where groups of up to twenty birds are regularly found. It is uncommon inland, but is sometimes found on the larger river systems, lakes, tarns and reservoirs. It is a sporadic Spring and Winter visitor to coastal sites.

Highest figures for the period come from the Kent Estuary with *thirty-four,* 31 Jul, 1973 on Arnside Marsh and the Inner Solway with *twenty-six,* 5 Aug, 1976 at Port Carlisle. Numbers on the Kent seem to have declined in recent years.

Lesser Yellowlegs *(Tringa flavipes)* *Vagrant*

A bird identified as this species at a gravel pit near Barrow, 20 Aug, 1971 by K Brown (LBR 71, No 62). The record was accepted by BBRC. This was the first and only record for Cumbria to date.

Green Sandpiper *(Tringa ochropus)*   *Passage migrant*

Although this bird is a regular visitor from June to September in suitable habitat, it is uncommon in Spring. In recent years it has been found over-wintering in the Inner Solway area, along the Duddon and in the Lyth and Kent valleys in the south. During this time the birds have been found on salt-marsh creeks, river banks and sewage farms. In the Autumn it is also found at reservoirs and estuarine sites.

It is usually found in small numbers, one or two birds at any one location, so *five,* 5 Aug, 1980 at Low Foulshaw; *five,* July 1982 at Longtown gravel pit and *c twelve,* July 1981 at Kirkby Pool in Furness are noteworthy records for the period under review.

Wood Sandpiper *(Tringa glareola)* Uncommon passage migrant

This scarce passage migrant may well be under recorded as it could, to the inexperienced observer, be over-looked. It prefers muddy river banks and reservoirs as well as estuarine sites. It is scarce inland, the only records for the period being *one,* 3 Jul, 1963 on a roadside pool near the River Eden, Mallerstang (P J Dare), *one,* 22 May, 1980 on the River Sprint, Burneside, near Kendal (P J Robinson) and *one,* 26 Jun, 1982 Broughton Moor, near Workington (A B Old).

Most birds are recorded on autumn passage between late June and September which normally involves solitary birds. The exception to this being at Walney Bird Observatory where *eight,* 14 Sep, 1970 and *eleven,* 13-14 Aug, 1980 were recorded, a few birds remaining into October.

Spring records are scarce and apart from the Burneside bird there is only *one,* 16 May, 1982, Castle Head, Grange-over-Sands (T H Jorgensen) and *one,* 1 May, 1983, Kirkby Pool (A A Cooper) during the period.

Common Sandpiper *(Tringa hypoleucos)*   *Breeding summer*
                                              visitor and passage migrant

The Common Sandpiper is a summer visitor to the county arriving in April and departing in mid-September. It is a scattered migrant in Spring with small numbers moving from the coastline up the river systems to their breeding sites. Nest sites are usually by rivers, streams, tarns and lakesides. Return passage begins in July and large groups can be found on the estuaries during July and August. Peak numbers during the period include *thirty-two,* 27 Jul, 1975, Meathop Marsh, Kent

Estuary; *thirty-seven,* 27 Jul, 1980, Esk Estuary and a remarkable *eighty-six,* 18 Jul, 1980, Duddon Estuary.

Eleven records of birds over-wintering in the county are recorded during the period.

Turnstone *(Arenaria interpres)Passage migrant and winter visitor*
This is a common bird along the coastline where there are boulder scars, mussel beds and plenty of seaweed. It is present in good numbers from August to May with some immature and non-breeding birds staying all summer.

It is a well travelled bird as ringing recoveries from the MBWG have come from Greenland, Iceland, Finland, Norway, Sweden, Denmark, France and Spain. Even more remarkable are three of their long distance recoveries during the period under review. A bird ringed 19 Aug, 1970 at Walney was picked up dead, 12 Dec, 1976 at Rabat, Morocco. Another bird ringed 4 Oct, 1970 at Aldingham was found dead on 2 Jun, 1976 over the Atlantic Ocean at Ellesmere Island, Canada. A second trans-atlantic bird was ringed 6 June,1974 at Alert, Canada and was recovered 29 Oct, 1977 on Walney Island.

After a period of stormy weather, birds can often be found on Cumbrian estuaries. Inland records are unusual so the following during the period are noteworthy;

One, 30 Jul, 1978, Sunbiggin Tarn (R I Kinley).
One, 8 May, 1980, Wet Sleddale Dam (D G Walker).
One, 6 May 1983, Longtown gravel pits (R Armstrong).

Red-necked Phalarope *(Phalaropus lobatus)* *Scarce spring and autumn migrant*
Stokoe's BLC noted this bird as being very rare with only five known records in the county. During the period under review another *fifteen* birds have been recorded. Six Spring records have occurred on the Inner Solway with another seven autumn records coming from between the Irt Estuary and Walney Island. Two records were at inland sites. They were *one,* 16 Oct, 1976, Ashness, Derwentwater (D Thomason) and *an immature,* 4-6 Aug, 1982, Sunbiggin Tarn (R Bottomley, R I Kinley *et al*).

Grey Phalarope *(Phalaropus fulicarius)* *Irregular passage migrant*
This bird is an uncommon migrant which usually appears between September and December, but is more often found after a series of October gales.

Most records have come from sites near to or along the coast and the birds involved only stay for a few days before moving on. An exception to this was an immature bird which stayed on the sea-front at Grange-over-Sands from 9 Dec, 1984 to 2 Jan, 1985. Although normally solitary birds, *three* were found on South Walney during early September, 1974, one of them was trapped and ringed.

It is very uncommon to find birds on inland sites, but the odd bird has been found on some of the county's lakes and reservoirs, particularly after a period of persistent gales. Records of birds on inland sites during the period include;

> *One,* 19-25 Oct, 1968, Sandford, Warcop (R W Robson, J W Allen) found in a flooded field.
>
> *One,* 22-25 Jan, 1979, Millerground, Lake Windermere (Mrs B M Taylor).

Pomarine Skua *(Stercorarius pomarinus)Scarce passage migrant*
No records were received of this Skua from along the coast between 1961, when a dead bird was picked up at Drumburgh on the Solway and a bird seen flying north past Walney Bird Observatory on 20 Jun, 1981. Since that date they have become an annual occurrence due to regular sea-watching at the Observatory with *one* bird being seen throughout the winter 1982/3.

Most records refer to autumn passage birds with only the odd spring bird having been seen. An extraordinary record of a storm-bound flock of *twenty-one* birds occurred on the Inner Solway on 3 May, 1982, when the birds were watched by M F Carrier as they went westwards against the gale down the estuary (Birds in Cumbria, Spring 1983, p 50).

Arctic Skua *(Stercorarius parasiticus)*   *Regular passage migrant*
This is the most regularly recorded Skua occurring along the Cumbrian coast, being seen between April and October. With regular sea-watching, several birds have been recorded as late as December with *one,* 2 Dec, 1979, Walney Bird Observatory and *one,* 19 Dec, 1982, Port Carlisle, Inner Solway (M F Carrier).

Inland records are unusual with a dead immature bird being found 16 Oct, 1961 on a farm at Crosthwaite, near Kendal and another immature bird staying in a field near Burneside from 2-5 Oct, 1976 (Birds in Cumbria, 1976-7). A bird was seen flying west over High Street by a party of fell-walkers, 7 May, 1978 (C Wells).

Long-tailed Skua *(Stercorarius longicaudus)*   *Rare passage migrant*

The only record during the last twenty years is of an immature bird seen off Grune Point, Solway on 30 Sep, 1967 (R Stokoe).

Two unpublished records which have recently come to light are;

Adult male, found dead under telegraph wires, Maryport, 30 Apr, 1947 (R Stokoe).

Adult, off St Bees Head, 24 May, 1957 (G W H Moule).

Great Skua *(Stercorarius skua)*   *Regular passage migrant*

Although not seen as frequently as the Arctic Skua, this bird is recorded annually along the coast between April and October. Odd wintering birds have also been recorded.

Sometimes birds will venture well up Cumbrian estuaries to harry Gulls and Terns of their food. Examples of this are;

Four, 16 Sep, 1978, Port Carlisle and *one,* 3 May, 1982, on the Inner Solway.

An *immature,* 15 Sep, 1974 at Sandside, Upper Kent Estuary with an *adult* at the same place, 17 Sep, 1978.

Mediterranean Gull *(Larus melanocephalus)*   *Rare visitor*

The arrival and spread of this Gull in the British Isles has taken place over the last twenty years, and was first recorded in the county in 1976. All the records to date are as follows;

Adult, 28 Jul, 1976, Arnside Marsh (D B Thexton).

Second year bird, 30 Jul, 1981, Foulney Island (A Phizaclea).

Adult, 13 & 25 Feb, 1982, Walney Bird Observatory (T Dean).

Adult, 11 Sep, 1983, High Foulshaw, Upper Kent Estuary (R Bottomley).

Adult, 11-12 Aug, 1984, Upper Kent Estuary (R Bottomley, M Hutcheson).

Adult, 1, 13 & 20 Sep, 1984, Walney Bird Observatory (T Dean).

Second year, 30 Sep, 1984, Selker Coastguard Station (A F Gould).

Laughing Gull *(Larus atricilla)*   *Vagrant*

The first two records of this vagrant American Gull occurred on the Kent Estuary during 1984.

First year bird, 27 May, 1984, flying down Kent Estuary (P J Marsh).

Second year bird, 14 Aug, 1984, High Foulshaw, Upper Kent Estuary (A F Gould).

There is a possibility that these two records refer to the same bird which could have moulted into second year plumage. Both records accepted by BBRC.

Little Gull *(Larus minutus)*   *Irregular passage migrant*

Most records of this attractive small gull have come from North Cumbria, with the Solway basin and the Eden Valley being most favoured. A Spring passage has been regularly recorded, although birds can be found between April and September. Sometimes small flocks are seen with *seven,* 13 May, 1974 at Sunbiggin Tarn; *eleven,* 23 May, 1974 off St Bees Head; *eleven,* 4 Jun, 1975, Rockcliffe Marsh; *six,* 13 Jun, 1980, Meathop, Kent Estuary and *eight,* 6 May, 1984, River Esk, Longtown.

Most of these birds are immatures with their distinctive wing markings.

Records of birds seen during the winter months are increasing, especially around the coast. *Two adults,* 21 Dec, 1976, Castlehead, Keswick (T B Wright) is most unusual.

Sabine's Gull *(Larus sabini)*   *Rare visitor*

Stokoe's BLC records four occasions when this rare arctic Gull has visited the county. The following have been recorded during the period under review;

   An immature, 28 Nov, 1980, Walney Bird Observatory with another *immature,* 8 Dec, 1984 (T Dean).

Black-headed Gull *(Larus ridibundus)*   *Resident and passage migrant*

This is one of the commonest Gulls being widespread throughout the county. It nests in several large and many small colonies on the coast and on inland tarns and mosses up to 1,200 ft. Breeding sites and numbers fluctuate as many sites have altering water levels due to drainage schemes or weather conditions. Human disturbance often controls numbers also.

There is a notable post-breeding movement to inland and coastal winter haunts. Large roosts are found on some lakes and estuaries which increase in number by passage migrants from the Continent.

Ringing has been done at many breeding sites and birds have been recovered from Heligoland, Norway, Denmark, Holland, Ireland, France and Spain.

Three foreign recoveries are;
   Bird ringed 14 Jun, 1959, Stavoren, Holland recovered
   23 Feb, 1969, Walney Bird Observatory.

Bird ringed 25 Jun, 1972, Limfjordan, Denmark, recovered dead, 1 Oct, 1975, Walney Island.
Bird ringed 11 Apr, 1980, Gdansk, Poland, found shot, 5 Mar, 1981, Workington.

Ring-billed Gull *(Larus delawarensis)*   *Vagrant*
As with the Laughing Gull, the first records of this vagrant American Gull occurred during 1984. This is not too surprising as the bird is becoming a regular visitor elsewhere in Britain, especially in Cornwall and Northern Ireland.

Adult, 15-18 Apr, 1984, Walney Bird Observatory with another adult at same site 26-27 Dec, 1984. *Adult,* 23 Dec, 1984 at Rampside (T Dean).

It is possible that these three records refer to the same bird.

Common Gull *(Larus canus)*   *Winter visitor and passage migrant.*
This bird can be seen from early July to late May. The first flocks of post-breeding birds appear during July and August and soon spread throughout the county, feeding on upland fields and gathering in large numbers on some of the lakes and estuaries to roost.

Stokoes BLC refers to the Common Gull as having bred on the Solway Marshes and at Ravenglass before the War. An odd pair bred on Crummock Water during 1977 and 1981 also at Easedale Tarn, Grasmere in 1977.

A bird found dead on 13 Nov, 1969, Fishcarling Point, Kent Estuary was ringed on 5 Jul, 1956 at Hornidal, Norway, making it just over thirteen years old.

Lesser Black-backed Gull *(Larus fuscus)* *Breeding visitor and passage bird*
During the period, the large nesting colony on Walney Island increased to a peak of *c twenty-five thousand* pairs in 1972 and represents the largest colony in Europe. In the last ten years numbers are slowly declining to the present total of around *c seventeen thousand* pairs. Formation of a new small colony on Haweswater is also noteworthy.

This Gull also nests in small numbers elsewhere along the coast with odd pairs nesting on saltmarshes, coastal mosses and moorland sites.

Ringing recoveries have shown that the majority of birds spend the winter months in Southern Europe and North Africa. Walney recoveries have come from seven countries in the area, one of the furthest being a bird ringed 8 Jul, 1968 which was found dead on 6 Jan, 1978 at Lagos, Nigeria.

It would seem that more birds are over-wintering in Britain in recent years as both adults and immatures can be found on estuaries, lakes and around towns, being most frequent at local refuse tips.

The continental race *(Larus fuscus graellsii)* occurs as an occasional passage migrant usually during the winter months.

Herring Gull *(Larus argentatus)   Resident and passage migrant*
Like the last species, the Herring Gull's stronghold is on Walney Island where a peak of twenty-four thousand pairs was recorded in 1978. Since then numbers have declined a little.

It is a numerous bird around the coast and estuaries of the county with a large colony of around *two thousand* pairs at St Bees Head. It also nests in small numbers on saltmarshes and coastal mosses with the odd record of pairs nesting on buildings in recent years in Carlisle and Barrow. A few pairs also breed with Lesser Black-backed Gulls on Haweswater.

Large post-breeding flocks have been recorded on the Solway with *c ten thousand three hundred* at Cardurnock on 13 Jul, 1980. This is a part of the annual move south in the Autumn mainly involving immature birds.

Adult birds are normally loyal to one breeding site, returning there each Spring. It is interesting to record a breeding female which was found in a colony in Jutland, Denmark was ringed as a chick on Walney Island nine years earlier.

An albino bird which at first was thought to be an Iceland Gull was seen and determined on 23-30 Dec, 1978 by M F Carrier at Longtown.

Small numbers over-winter inland as revealed by gull-roost counts at the larger lakes in the county, with *c one hundred,* Nov/Dec, 1980 on Derwentwater and *c two hundred,* 15 Jan, 1980 at Millerground, Lake Windermere.

Iceland Gull *(Larus glaucoides)*   *Rare winter visitor*
Stokoe's BLC notes only six records of this scarce winter bird. During the period under review a further nine have been seen.

> *Adult,* 21 Dec, 1963, Walney Bird Observatory (B Sutton).
> *Second year,* 13 May-6 Jun, 1979, Rockcliffe Marsh (D Bailey, J Kirk, J Willis).

First year, 19 Apr, 1980, Hodbarrow (P J Marsh).
First year, 22-31 Mar, 1983, Maryport harbour (I Livingstone, M Copley).
First year, 18 Apr, 1983, Sellafield (A. Strand).
First year, 3 Mar, 1984, Workington pier (J C Callion).
Third year, 20 Mar-17 Apr, 1984, Whitehaven harbour (R S Wimpress).
First year, 17 Apr, 1984, Walney Bird Observatory (T Dean),
Second year, 29 Apr, 1984, Siddick (S. Richardson).
Careful observation must be made with this bird as confusion can occur with the albino form of the Herring Gull.

Glaucous Gull *(Larus hyperboreus)*   *Irregular winter visitor*
Records of this large northern Gull have been infrequent up to the last ten years when numbers of reports of sightings have increased annually. No less than fifteen individual records were recorded during the winter 1983/4.

All records have come from the coast, with the odd bird seen in the upper estuaries, like the Inner Solway and Upper Kent Estuary.

Inland records are rare with only one during the last twenty-five years. This was a bird seen flying into a westerly gale on 12 Nov, 1973 at Ormside in the Eden Valley by R W Robson.

Great Black-backed Gull *(Larus marinus)Resident and winter*
                                                                                 passage bird
This large gull is a scarce breeding bird in the county with a few pairs nesting each year on Rockcliffe Marsh and *c ten* pairs on Walney Island. Non-breeding birds often gather in estuaries and other sites in small flocks of *c seventy* birds, during the summer months. During the Autumn and early part of the winter these flocks increase in number as immature birds join them. Figures from BOEE counts during 1984 found *c two hundred* on the Solway in October, *c one hundred and thirty* on the Duddon in November, *c two hundred* on the Leven in September and *c three hundred and fifty* on the Kent during the same month. Walney Island held *c one hundred and sixty* during December.

Ringing recoveries often reveal this bird to be a long distance traveller, an example being a bird recovered on Walney Island during 1959, which was ringed at Murmansk, Russia the year before.

Kittiwake *(Rissa tridactyla)*   *Breeding and passage migrant*

The Kittiwake's only nesting site in Cumbria is St Bees Head, where numbers have fallen during the last thirty years from *c one thousand six hundred* in 1956 to *c eight hundred and ten* in 1984.

Passage birds are recorded along the coast in Spring and Autumn from Walney Island to the Solway, sometimes in large numbers. *c three hundred* moving south, 9 Sep, 1984 at Walney Bird Observatory.

In stormy conditions, the bird can suffer quite badly, particularly in the winter months when birds may perish in moderate numbers. Many birds are also blown well inland *ten,* 2 May, 1982 at Sunbiggin Tarn and *seventy-five* flying east, 26 Jan, 1983 over the Inner Solway.

Ivory Gull *(Pagophila eburnea)*   *Vagrant*

Macpherson's VFL refers to a very old record of an adult at Cunswick Tarn, near Kendal around 1850.

Sandwich Tern *(Sterna sandvicensis)*   *Breeding visitor and*
passage migrant

The Sandwich Tern arrives in early April and stays until late September, with the odd few seen in October. A very early bird was *one,* 18 Mar, 1975 on the Duddon.

The well documented colony of breeding birds at Drigg (Stokoe BLC) rose from *four hundred and eighty* pairs in 1956 to *seven hundred and eight* pairs in 1976. This figure was down to *one hundred and thirty-six* pairs in 1977 and they have not bred at this site since. A smaller colony on Foulney Island was decimated by rats in the 1960's, but wardening and conservation by the Cumbria Trust for Nature Conservation saw the return of the bird in 1976 when *one hundred and fifty* pairs bred. This built up to *c six hundred* pairs in 1978 and in 1984 stands at *c one thousand* pairs. Smaller numbers breed sporadically on the Duddon and Walney Island, where *two hundred and fifty* pairs bred in 1972.

Passage birds are occasionally found well up river estuaries although they are rarely seen inland. Records in the period include *three* different birds over Carlisle in 1979 and 1980; an *immature* bird, 12 Sep, 1976 at Whinfell Tarn, near Kendal and *three,* 4 May, 1978 at Killington Reservoir, which came in to roost at dusk (A F Gould).

Cumbrian ringed birds have been recovered in six south-west African countries. A juvenile ringed 17 Jul, 1963 on

Foulney Island was found nesting, 30 May, 1971 on the Friesian Isles, Holland.

Roseate Tern *(Sterna dougallii)*   *Scarce passage migrant*
This is not a common bird in Cumbria, particularly in recent years when only the odd bird is recorded each year. Most records come from the Walney/Foulney Island area and *two* pairs bred on Foulney Island during 1970 (M E Greenhalgh) with the other terns.

Inland records are rare, so *two*, 8 Aug, 1981 at Longtown gravel pits is unusual.

Common Tern *(Sterna hirundo)*   *Passage migrant and breeding visitor*
This is a regular breeding bird at a Solway site, *c fifty* pairs and Foulney Island, *c one hundred to one hundred and twenty* pairs, with several smaller colonies at other estuarine locations.

Breeding numbers fluctuate from year to year as like most terns they suffer from predation and disturbance frequently.

The Common Tern is seen regularly inland during Spring and Autumn passage, suggesting possible cross-country flight lines from east to west and return.

Arctic Tern *(Sterna paradisaea)*   *Passage migrant and breeding visitor*
The Arctic Tern breeds in association with the Common Tern at several of their colonies, the largest numbers being at Foulney Island where around *c eighty* pairs breed.

The birds are to be found nesting on the fringes of the Common Tern colonies.

During passage movements it will also participate with Common Terns, especially in gale conditions when larger numbers can be seen well up the estuaries.

Inland records are not common. A most unusual record is of *two* birds flying south-west at 2,800 ft. over the summit of Fairfield on 28 Sep, 1974. Other records inland during the period include *one*, 7 Sep, 1976 at Wray, Lake Windermere; *one*, 29 Aug, 1977 at Tarn House Tarn, Kirkby Stephen; *one*, 3 May, 1982, Haweswater; *one*, 31 May 1982, River Wampool, Dalston; and *one*, 18 Sep, 1982 at Longtown gravel pits.

Sooty Tern *(Sterna fuscata)*   *Vagrant*
Stokoe's BLC refers to a record of this species at Drigg Point during June 1933.

Little Tern *(Sterna albifrons)* *Passage migrant and breeding visitor*

A number of pairs of Little Terns are successful in breeding each year on the quieter parts of the coast from Grune Point to Foulney Island. It is the most vulnerable of all the terns as it tends to breed on shingle beaches at around the height of the Spring tide-line. At this level the breeding success is jeopardised by high tides in June and the continual threat from all sorts of disturbance. 1984 was a good year as *seventy five* pairs reared *seventy-three* flying young.

Inland records are rare with *three,* 10 Sep, 1974 on Arnside Marsh and *one,* 21 Sep, 1981 at Killington Reservoir.

Whiskered Tern *(Chlidonias hybrida)* *Vagrant*
A bird of this species was identified by W French and A W Vincent on 13 May, 1957 at Tindale Tarn.

Black Tern *(Chlidonias niger)* *Sparse passage migrant*
The Black Tern was recorded as a breeding bird in the old county of Cumberland in the nineteenth century. Currently it is recorded as an irregular spring and autumn migrant.

It frequents rivers, lakes, tarns and estuaries and has been seen with 'Sterna' terns on the coast. It is most frequent in the Solway Basin which suggests a cross-country movement. Immature birds are usually involved in the autumn migration.

Records usually involve one or two birds, so *sixteen,* 4 Jun, 1970 at Rockcliffe Marsh (L T Colley) seen flying in an easterly direction, and *thirteen,* 29 Sep, 1982 at Longtown gravel pits, are outstanding.

Several records of late migrants occurring in November have been reported during the period under review, they include:

Two, 4 Nov, 1967, West Plain, Flookburgh; *one,* 27 Oct-1 Nov, 1969, Sandside, Kent Estuary; *one,* 5 Nov, 1977, River Eden, Rickerby Park, Carlisle; *one,* 27 Oct-16 Nov, 1977, Blelham Tarn and *one,* 18 Nov, 1984, Esthwaite Water.

White-winged Black Tern *(Chlidonias leucopterus)* *Vagrant*
Stokoe's BLC refers to an old record of a bird seen in May 1913 at Skinburness.

Guillemot *(Uria aalge)* *Passage migrant and breeding bird.*
Breeding numbers of Guillemot on St Bees Head seem to be fairly constant over the last twenty years, with around *two*

thousand five hundred pairs in 1974 and 1979 with *two thousand seven hundred and ten* pairs in 1984. Stokoe's BLC quotes *two thousand and ten* pairs in 1956.

During the winter months, small numbers can be found on the Solway and between the Duddon and Morecambe Bay. Birds are sometimes found in the estuaries after adverse weather conditions or if they are ailing or oiled. Inland records are rare.

Razorbill *(Alca torda)*   *Passage migrant and breeding bird*

Although less numerous than the Guillemot, numbers of breeding pairs of Razorbill on St Bees Head are stable with *c one hundred and ten to one hundred and fifty* pairs each year.

Small numbers spend the winter months around the Cumbrian coast, the most favoured area being the disturbed waters around Walney Island. Storm-bound, oiled and ailing birds are occasionally found in the estuaries. Inland records are rare.

Black Guillemot *(Cepphus grylle)*   *Local breeding bird and passage migrant*

St Bees Head represents the southernmost breeding site of Black Guillemot on the west coast of Britain. Although only around *four* pairs breed each year, birds are often encountered along the coast from the Solway to Morecambe Bay. During April 1980, *two* adults and an *immature* bird were seen in the Walney-Foulney Island area.

Away from the coast it is scarce, the only record for the period being a *sick bird,* 24 Sep, 1968 at Arnside Viaduct.

Little Auk *(Alle alle)*   *Scarce winter visitor*

The Little Auk is an irregular winter visitor to the Cumbrian coast, most records referring to storm driven birds. In a period of winter gales birds are often blown well inland with casualties appearing along the coast.

Passage migrants are occasionally seen along the coast, especially off Walney Island. Only small numbers of birds are recorded on these occasions with *sixteen,* 8 Mar, 1981 being exceptional, but should encourage future 'sea-watchers' to be vigilant.

Records of storm-bound birds in the period include; *one,* 23 Nov, 1955, River Eden, Appleby (W R Robinson); *one,* 13 Nov, 1982, Distington (R S Wimpress); *one,* 21 Dec, 1982, Ferry House, Lake Windermere (Miss K M Atkinson); *one,* 9 Feb, 1983, Argill, South Stainmore — dead (A Coulthurst);

one, 7 Feb, 1983, Dentdale (C Armistead, J Bolton) – this bird later released on Morecambe Bay; *one,* 13-14 Feb, 1983, Coatlap Point, Lake Windermere (C R Honour); *one,* 15 Jan, 1984, Gosforth (A Strand); *one,* 20 Jan, 1984, Oddendale Quarry, Crosby Ravensworth (A J Gardiner).

Puffin *(Fratercula arctica)*   *Sparse breeding bird and winter visitor*

Only a small number of Puffin breed at St. Bees Head each year, with around *twelve to fifteen* pairs being the constant figure.

Like all members of the 'auk' family, the Puffin is often a casualty during a period of storms, but rarely is it found inland.

Away from St Bees area, it is irregularly recorded as a passage migrant, particularly around Walney Island. Winter birds have been seen in recent years in small numbers since the first report came from the Walney Bird Observatory in 1977.

Pallas's Sandgrouse *(Syrrhaptes paradoxus)*   *Vagrant*

This bird has not been recorded since the great irruptions of 1863 and 1888, although *two* birds claimed on 7 and 8 Jun, 1969 at Braithwaite Bog *(per* A Barton) (BB, Vol 63, p 281) has never been authenticated.

Rock Dove *(Columba livia)*

A former infrequent visitor to the Solway region from Scottish coastal colonies. Today most birds found are hybrids with feral pigeons which occur widely in the county.

Stock Dove *(Columba oenas)*   *Resident and winter passage bird*

The Stock Dove is fairly common throughout the county, especially in areas of arable farmland. Passage birds in the Autumn and Winter months add to the population with flocks of up to a *hundred* birds being found on occasion, particularly in the arable areas. Elsewhere, the bird is found on fell-side crags as well as coastal cliffs and sand dune systems.

Woodpigeon *(Columba palumbus)Resident and passage migrant*

The Woodpigeon is common and widespread throughout the county as a breeding bird and occurs from the coastal regions to the Pennine foothills where suitable cover can be found. Where tree cover is sparse, birds have been seen to nest in hawthorn and gorse bushes with the odd nest being built on the ground.

During the Autumn and Winter months the local population increases enormously with migrant birds from the north. Flocks often reach a *thousand* or more birds in areas where green brassica fodder is grown for farm animals and in deciduous woodland where flocks can be found feeding on acorns, beech mast, ivy and other berries.

Collared Dove *(Streptopelia decaocto)*   *Resident*

Stokoe's BLC relates the first breeding record of the Collared Dove being at a Solway coastal village in July 1959.

Since that date the bird has become fairly common throughout most of the county, particularly so in towns, villages and around large farms. It is a great opportunist and has become firmly established in the county as a breeding bird within the last twenty-five years.

In winter birds will often form communal roosts in churchyards, large gardens etc. where there is evergreen cover. Up to a *hundred* birds have been recorded in such roosts.

Turtle Dove *(Streptopelia turtur)*   *Scarce passage migrant*

The Turtle Dove is an irregular summer migrant in Cumbria. It occurs most frequently in the low lying coastal areas and in the Eden Valley. Most birds are seen in May, but recent records have occurred from late April to October. Records often refer to *single* birds which have been found in company with Collared Doves or Woodpigeon.

A recent noteworthy record is of *three* birds flying in off the sea at Silecroft on 4 Oct, 1981 (A F Gould).

There have been no breeding records during the period under review and Stokoe's BLC states that the last recorded breeding pair was in Cumberland in 1951.

Overwintering is unusual in the British Isles, so a bird found with Collared Doves in Barrow-in-Furness between 23 and 25 Dec, 1980 (B Sutton, J Sheldon) is of note.

Great Spotted Cuckoo *(Clamator glandarius)*   *Vagrant*

Stokoe's BLC records an adult male seen at close quarters by Major Charles Graham at Croft Head, Netherby on 26 Jun, 1960.

Unfortunately, the record was not accepted by BBRC due to lack of detail and must remain 'underlined'.

Cuckoo *(Cuculus canorus)*   *Summer visitor and passage migrant*
The Cuckoo is a breeding visitor from April to September,with immature birds being recorded as late as November.

A decline of this bird has been recorded in some districts in recent years, but it is still fairly widespread around the coastal regions and on the lower fellsides in the Lake District and the Pennines.

An early migrant was recorded at Eskmeals Nature Reserve on 28 Mar, 1978.

Barn Owl *(Tyto alba)*   *Resident*
This bird was described in Stokoe's BLC as 'common throughout the county', but sadly this handsome owl has declined most noticeably in the last twenty years. It can now be classified as infrequent, locally common in a few areas to the north and west of the county. Suggested causes for the decline include habitat loss, persecution, disturbance and pesticides (BWP, Vol 4, p 434).

Favoured breeding sites include old farm and other buildings, hollow trees and occasionally at higher levels, rocky gullies and crags.

Scops Owl *(Otus scops)*   *Vagrant*
Stokoe's BLC refers to two old records plus a bird seen at the edge of a wood near Kendal, 18 Dec, 1956 (J W Allen) (Field Naturalist, Vol 2, No 1).

A bird was claimed to have been seen, heard calling and recorded on 8 and 9 Apr, 1966 at Ravenstonedale (Mrs P Shepard). The record has not been submitted to BBRC as the details are now unavailable.

Snowy Owl *(Nyctea scandiaca)*   *Vagrant*
Stokoe's BLC lists two old records in 1930 and 1959.

Little Owl *(Athene noctua)*   *Resident*
The Little Owl is widespread in its distribution in the county, although it has not become a common bird anywhere. It is most often found in areas of mixed agriculture and parkland, favouring the lowland areas of the county, particularly along the coast.

Breeding sites include coastal cliffs, old quarries, derelict buildings, drystone walls and hollow trees.

Tawny Owl *(Strix aluco)*   *Resident*

This Owl is common and widespread throughout the county, being locally known as the Brown Owl. It is basically a woodland bird but is found in many habitats including the centres of towns and villages.

It uses barns, derelict buildings and hollow trees as breeding sites, often using a safe site annually. It has also been known to nest on the ground in some of these situations.

The Tawny Owl can live to a good age for example a nestling ringed by J W Allen in Levens Park in May 1960 was found as a road victim at Brigsteer, 16th Mar, 1974.

Long-eared Owl *(Asio otus)*   *Scarce resident, passage migrant*

This is an uncommon Owl in Cumbria, breeding sparsely in remote mainly coniferous woodland.

Passage birds are recorded occasionally along the coast in Autumn and one or two winter coastal roost sites, containing up to *six* birds, have been known during the period under review.

A bird ringed at Walney Bird Observatory on 5 Dec, 1976 was recovered on the Trans Siberian Railway near Ronga, Mariskaya, USSR on 25 Aug, 1978. This is approximately 2,000 miles and is the longest distance recorded of a migrant Long-eared Owl from Britain.

Short-eared Owl *(Asio flammeus)*   *Resident, passage migrant and winter visitor*

The Short-eared Owl is an irregular breeding bird of the lower fellsides and moorland. Most records coming from the Border Hills, coastal mosses and Pennine foothills.

Passage birds are seen from September to April and can be found around young forestry plantations, coastal sand dune systems, heaths, bogs and marshes. It can often be found hunting during the daylight hours with up to ten birds being seen together in favoured localities, where the vole population is high.

It often migrates the length of Europe, an example being a bird ringed at Walney Bird Observatory on 23 Sep, 1972 was killed at Benavente, Spain on 27 Nov, two months later.

Pellets found in a winter roost at Rampside in 1980 contained the rings of a Turnstone and two British, a Swedish and a Norwegian Dunlin.

Tengmalm's Owl *(Aegolius funereus)*   *Vagrant*

Macpherson VFL relates an old record of a female shot at Gosforth, 3 Nov, 1876.

Nightjar *(Caprimulgus europaeus) Scarce breeding summer visitor*
Once a common summer visitor to Cumbrian mosses, woodland fringes and limestone fellsides, the Nightjar has become a scarce bird. The decline has been very notable during the last twenty years and as a result, the BTO Nightjar Census in 1981 revealed only eight breeding sites in the county. Most of these records came from the coastal mosses, further inland the bird has become very uncommon.

Swift *(Apus apus)*   *Breeding summer migrant*
A common summer visitor, arriving in May and departing in late August with stragglers being seen into November.

It nests mainly under the roof spaces of older buildings. It has also been known to use mine galleries and a river gorge crag in the Eden Valley.

Passage birds are often observed moving in regular numbers along the coastline, river valleys and over the highest fell tops. Poor weather conditions will bring large numbers over lakes and reservoirs for a short time, *c two thousand* over Lake Windermere, 21 May, 1979, being an example of this.

Alpine Swift *(Apus melba)*   *Vagrant*
Macpherson VFL relates an old record of a bird being shot at Low Mill House, Egremont on 4 Jul, 1842. The only other records are;

    One, 17 Jun, 1957, Grange-over-Sands (H A F Thompson)
    One, 4 Oct, 1965, Dalton-in-Furness (A L Evans)
    One, 26 Jul, 1970, Barrow-in-Furness (K Brown)

Kingfisher *(Alcedo atthis)*   *Resident*
The Kingfisher is not a common bird, with numbers fluctuating from year to year. There has been a tendency towards a decline in numbers over the last twenty years, as it has suffered badly the severe winters of 1976/7 and 1981/2.

It prefers the slower rivers and streams, but during the Autumn and Winter months can be found around the larger lakes, in estuarine creeks and along the coast.

A bird was found at over 1,000 ft. on Blea Tarn, Langdale on 23 Jan, 1977.

Bee-eater *(Merops apiaster)*   *Vagrant*
There are two records for the county of this colourful bird, both occurring during the last fifteen years.

A *single* bird was found on 2 Aug, 1970 at Millwood, Barrow-in-Furness by K Brown. The second record was of *four* adults seen on 8 Jun, 1981 at Sizergh Castle by A. Michelini, M Hutcheson and A F Gould. These birds were seen feeding and preening in the orchard of the Castle, before disappearing after a brief but memorable visit.

Both records have been accepted by the BBRC.

Bee-eater.

Roller *(Coracias garrulus)*   *Vagrant*

There are seven records to date of the Roller occurring in Cumbria. Stokoe's BLC refers to five old records as well as a sixth individual which occurred at Mungrisedale on 15 Mar, 1953 (G E Hall) (Lakeland Birds, 1958, p 20).

A bird found near Armathwaite Hall, on the shore of Bassenthwaite Lake, by Mr & Mrs J B Wharton on 25 Sep, 1982, remained in the area until 29 Sep and was seen by many local observers. This record was accepted by BBRC (Birds in Cumbria, Spring 1983, p 31).

Hoopoe *(Upupa epops)*   *Scarce passage migrant.*

There have been eleven records of this obvious, but irregular, passage migrant in the period under review. Records are of *single* birds and are recorded during the months of April to June and August to October.

Wryneck *(Jynx torquilla)*   *Scarce passage migrant.*

Stokoe's BLC quotes this former breeding migrant as rare, with only three 'recent' records. During the last twenty years there have been a further twenty records with birds being seen during May, June and August to early November. Substantial numbers were recorded throughout Britain during the Autumn of 1976 when five individual records were reported from a wide area of Cumbria (Birds in Cumbria, 1976-7).

Green Woodpecker *(Picus viridis)*   *Resident*

Although a rarity at the beginning of the century, the spread of the Green Woodpecker northwards through the county is noteworthy. It is a regular bird of parkland and deciduous woodland in the central and southern parts of the county. Further north in the Solway Basin and towards the Scottish Border it is not as common. In the Lake District and the Eden Valley it has been known to nest on fellsides up to 1,000 ft.

There has been the occasional coastal movement of this bird recorded in the county, an example being an *adult* and an *immature* bird seen at either end of Walney Island during August 1982 (Birds in Cumbria, Spring 1983)

Great Spotted Woodpecker *(Dendrocopos major)*   *Resident*

This Woodpecker can be found throughout the county. It is fairly common especially in parts of open countryside and woodland where there are dead trees. It is not a bird of coniferous woodland.

During the winter months it is frequently found in suburban gardens, often visiting bird-tables. At this time it can also be found foraging along hedgerows.

Coastal passage is occasionally recorded, especially during October and November when the British population is supplemented by birds from Scandinavia.

Lesser Spotted Woodpecker *(Dendrocopos minor)* *Uncommon resident*

This is the least common of our three resident Woodpeckers. Breeding records are sparse, only coming from a few sites in open woodland around the lakes of Ullswater, Rydal, Grasmere, Windermere and Coniston and in the southern river valleys.

It is rarely seen elsewhere in the county away from these sites.

Woodlark *(Lullula arborea)*   *Rare summer migrant*

Once a former breeding bird in suitable terrain, the Woodlark has now become a rarity in Cumbria. The last known record is of a bird which spent three weeks in May 1959 near Sedbergh (Field Naturalist, Vol 4, No 6).

Skylark *(Alauda arvensis)*   *Resident, winter passage bird*

The Skylark is a breeding bird of open grassland areas from the coast to the high fellsides, where it can be found up to 2,000 ft.

Many of our breeding birds emigrate during the Autumn. During the winter, large flocks congregate in stubble fields, saltmarshes and along the coast, many of the birds coming here from Northern Europe. A lot of these birds move on to Ireland, Southern England and the Continent in severe conditions. A *thousand* birds per hour were recorded moving south down the coast at Whitehaven on 14 Dec, 1981 by R S Wimpress and *one thousand two hundred* birds were in the vicinity of the Walney Bird Observatory on 24 Jan, 1984.

Shore Lark *(Eremophila alpestris)*   *Rare winter visitor*
Stokoe's BLC quotes nine records of this uncommon bird to our coast as having been seen between November and March, an exception being a bird at Skinburness in May 1920.

During the last twenty years, a further nine records have been submitted. Most of these are of single individuals, with *two* 28 Nov, 1976 at Grune Point and *three* Jan/Feb, 1977 and 15 Dec, 1981 at Walney Bird Observatory.

A most unusual record during the period under review is of a male in summer plumage found on the summit of Blencathra on 28 Oct, 1971 by K R Gabriel and R J Walton.

Sand Martin *(Riparia riparia)*   *Breeding summer migrant*
A regular breeding bird at suitable sites, which include river banks, sand and gravel pits. It also uses a few artificial sites like drainage pipes. Breeding is also recorded from the sandstone sea-cliffs at St Bees. Availability of breeding sites throughout the county are scarce, particularly in the central Lake District area. This is not helped by the Water Authority in some districts proceeding with a policy of strengthening and landscaping river banks, which in turn has destroyed known breeding sites. An example of this being the Kendal flood relief scheme which on its completion destroyed three small colonies.

A decline in numbers has been recorded over the last twenty years which is country-wide. A drastic fall in numbers occurred in Spring 1984 when as high as 80% of the 1983 population failed to return to their breeding sites.

Two colonies in the north-east of the county monitored by M F Carrier were typical of the countrywide situation. One site at Faugh had *c three hundred* pairs in 1983 and was down to *nineteen* pairs and the other site at Midgeholme had no breeding birds at all in a site with *sixty-five* pairs in the previous year. The BTO explained the cause as the terrible drought conditions which occurred in the vicinity of their wintering grounds in the Sahel area of Western Africa.

A young bird ringed at Faugh, 23 Jul, 1982 was retrapped there on 30 May, 1983 and retrapped again on 25 Aug, 1983, at Chareute, Maritime, France (1071 km.).

Swallow *(Hirundo rustica)*   *Breeding summer migrant*
This is a widespread and regular breeding summer visitor. It breeds in barns, out-houses and other buildings where pairs will often have two broods and if the conditions are right, three.

It is often to be found near water, particularly during migration when birds will use river valleys as a flight lane and lakes, tarns and reservoirs as a feeding ground.

The first Spring migrants usually arrive during the first weeks of April with the odd record in late March. The earliest date during the period being a bird seen over Bassenthwaite Lake, 21 Mar, 1976 (B & S Richardson). The return Autumn migration is during September and October, with odd birds remaining into November. The latest date is the only December record for the county, when a bird was seen at Hodbarrow on 1 Dec, 1984 (R I Kinley, T Kirk, D B Thexton).

Large roosts are often formed in favoured reed-beds during migration. The Swallow is a well known long distance traveller as is shown by a bird ringed at Appleby on 1 Jul, 1979. It was found dead on 15 Jan, 1980 at Fraserburgh, Cape Province, South Africa (9882 km.).

Occasionally albino Swallows are found. Recent records include a bird at Walney Bird Observatory on 30 and 31 Jul, 1980; *one,* Rusland, 31 Aug, 1981 (C J Band); and *one,* Ratherheath Tarn, Kendal, 1 Sep, 1981 (S T Robinson). The last two records possibly refer to the same bird.

House Martin *(Delichon urbica)*   *Breeding summer migrant*
The House Martin is a regular breeding summer visitor throughout the county. It has been reported to be declining in some areas during the last twenty years, although no drastic reduction in numbers has been recorded.

The traditional breeding site, under the eaves of buildings, is most regularly used in the region, although several quarry sites have been used as well as the cliff sites of St Bees Head and Whitbarrow Scar.

Migration takes place in April, September and October. November records are noteworthy, but not too infrequent.

A late breeding *pair* was recorded by A F Gould during November 1977 in Kendal. *Four* fledged young were on the wing with their parents on 14 Nov. The birds were last seen on 16 Nov.

The only December record is of a 'tired' bird flying around Stricklandgate, Kendal, on 8 Dec, 1979 (A F Gould).

During migration, communal roosting in trees has occasionally been recorded. An example being *c fifty* birds in trees around Esthwaite Water on 18 Apr, 1979 (Miss K M Atkinson).

An albino bird was seen at Satterthwaite on 26 Sep, 1978 (D & J A Greenaway).

Richard's Pipit *(Anthus novaeseelandiae)* *Rare passage migrant*
Stokoe's BLC quotes six records of this large Asiatic Pipit, all in the Solway region between Allonby and Bowness-on-Solway.

During the last twenty years three more records have been added;

> *One,* 8-10 Nov, 1980, Walney Bird Observatory, with a second bird at the same site over-wintering from 28 Nov, 1980-14 Jan, 1981.

The third record is rather unusually a Spring record of a bird seen 4 May, 1984 at Sandscales Haws (K Morton). Most Richard's Pipit records occur in Autumn with only 1.5% appearing during April/May to date.

Tawny Pipit *(Anthus campestris)* *Rare passage migrant*
This rare migrant Pipit has only been recorded four times in the county, all at Walney Bird Observatory and within the last five years. This is possibly due to better observation by the increase in birdwatchers, rather than the bird's rarity.

The dates were; 18 Oct, 1980; 9 Aug, 1982; 27 Aug, 1982 and 1 Sep, 1984.

All have been accepted by the BBRC.

Tree Pipit *(Anthus trivialis)* *Summer breeding migrant*
This is a bird of open ground with scattered trees, such as the mosses in the north of the county and the limestone scars in the south. It also frequents open parts of woodland and railway embankments.

It is a widespread bird, locally common, which arrives in April and departs in early October.

Passage movement is often substantial at Walney Bird Observatory with up to *forty* birds a day having been recorded during September.

Meadow Pipit *(Anthus pratensis)*   *Resident and winter visitor*
The Meadow Pipit is widely distributed throughout the county. It can be found on rough ground, grassland, moorland and on open fellsides up to 3000 ft. It is also common at lower levels, being a regular bird of the coastal headlands and estuarine saltmarshes.

Most birds breeding on high ground leave their sites in September and return to them in March. This gives rise to large numbers on passage along the coast each Spring and Autumn. It is a particularly noteworthy feature at Walney Bird Observatory during the Autumn where an average of *ten thousand* birds pass through each year.

Hard weather movements can also bring large numbers into a small locality. This occurred during Spring 1981, when heavy snowfall on 25 Apr forced *c five hundred* birds into two fields by Borrowdale Road, Keswick (S C Turnbull) and *several hundred* were seen on school playing fields in Kendal with other migrants (A F Gould).

An albino was found with other pipits on 28 Mar, 1979 at Hoathwaite, Torver (L Grisedale).

Ringing recoveries from Walney Bird Observatory includes three birds from Spain.

Rock Pipit *(Anthus spinoletta spinoletta)*   *Resident and passage migrant*
The coastal cliffs around St Bees Head is the stronghold for the Rock Pipit in Cumbria, where around *c fifteen* pairs breed each year. Other records involving one or two pairs, come from the Solway and around Walney Island.

Elsewhere it is found as a passage migrant, particularly in winter, when it is to be found well up the estuaries of the Inner Solway and Morecambe Bay, looking for food along the tide-line.

Water Pipit *(Anthus spinoletta petrosus)* *Scarce passage migrant*
The Water Pipit is a continental montane sub-species of the Rock Pipit which has not often been recorded in the county.

Although a sub-species its plumage is notably different, particularly in Spring with its pale underparts, eye-stripe and white outer tail feathers.

It is recorded as a scarce winter visitor and a passage

migrant in April. Stokoe's BLC notes only two records and five more have been added under the period under review;

One, 1 Apr, 1979, Loughrigg Fell (G Williams).
One, 2 Apr, 1980, Riggindale, Haweswater (P D Godolphin).
One, 5 Jan, 1981, Walney Bird Observatory.
One, 18 Dec, 1981, Walney Bird Observatory.
One, 4 Mar, 1984, Cavendish Dock, Barrow-in-Furness (C Johnston)

Yellow Wagtail *(Motacilla flava flavissima)   Breeding summer visitor and passage migrant*

This is a regular breeding bird of rough pastures and meadows, often near to water, up to 1,000 ft. It occurs throughout the county, but is less common in the Solway Basin.

Passage birds arrive in April and depart during September. As with other species of Wagtail, notable coastal passage is occasionally recorded. Walney Bird Observatory recorded *four hundred and eighty-five* birds during August 1980, with *forty* birds moving through on 26 Aug. Cold weather conditions in Spring also have an effect on passage with an example being *c seventy* 26 Apr, 1981 at Kendal Sewage Works (A F Gould) during a brief blizzard.

Two late records in 1978 were an *adult,* 18 Nov, at Aldingham (Furness) (Ms C Helm) and a *juvenile* 3-10 Dec, at Walney Bird Observatory.

The continental **Blue-headed Wagtail** *(Motacilla flava flava)* occurs infrequently during the passage migration periods. A pair of this race was recorded as having bred in the foothills of the Northern Pennines (M Tulloch) in 1983.

Grey Wagtail *(Motacilla cinerea)   Resident and passage migrant*

The Grey Wagtail is a bird of streams and swift flowing rivers where it can be found as a breeding bird up to 1,500 ft. in suitable habitat.

Most sites are deserted after the breeding season when family parties can be found on coastal and estuarine areas, although a few birds can be found throughout the winter months on the lower reaches of rivers in the south of the county.

Autumn pasage is most obvious in September when many birds move south along with migrant birds from Europe and Scandinavia.

Passage at Walney Bird Observatory was exceptional

during September 1980, when a total of *four hundred and forty-nine* birds passed through during the month, with a maximum of *sixty* on the 20th.

Pied Wagtail *(Motacilla alba yarrellii)*   *Resident and passage migrant*

The Pied Wagtail is a common breeding bird throughout the county. It is also a passage bird with notable migration being recorded in both Spring and Autumn.

As with the Grey Wagtail, birds breeding at higher levels leave during the Autumn, leaving only a small population to over-winter near the coast.

From Autumn to Spring, the Pied Wagtail roosts gregariously often involving *several hundred* birds at any one site. Reed-beds near water are a favourite site, but in towns, street trees and buildings are used. In the last ten years such sites have included Carlisle Citadel Railway Station, Southwaite Motorway Service Station, a few trees in the centre of Kendal and Burneside Paper Mill.

Migration often takes birds well down into Southern Europe, examples being birds ringed in August 1977 and 1978 being recovered in the following winter in Portugal and Southern Spain respectively.

White Wagtail *(Motacilla alba alba)*   *Passage migrant*

The White Wagtail is the continental race of the Pied Wagtail and can be found as a passage migrant between April and September. Like all wagtails it occurs near water, and is more often found near the coast.

Waxwing *(Bombycilla garrulus)*   *Irregular winter migrant*

The Waxwing is a sporadic winter visitor which sometimes occurs in large numbers or irruptions. In recent years it has been rather a scarce bird in Cumbria with the only 'irruption' year in the period being 1966, with good numbers around in 1974 and 1975.

Birds often feed in small flocks on berries such as Hawthorn, Yew, and Holly. They also favour cultivated plants like Cotoneaster, Pyracantha and Viburnum opulus. To find these they will often venture into town and suburban gardens, showing no apparent fear of man.

During 1966 birds were found in good numbers all over the county. Other notable flocks include *c one hundred,* 22-26 Dec, 1974 at Ulverston (J Sheldon), the largest number recorded in Furness; *forty-nine,* 18 Jan, 1975 at Stainton, Carlisle; *twenty-*

six, 8 Feb, 1975 at Great Asby and *twenty-three,* 26 Jan, 1976 in the Garburn Pass, Kentmere.

Dipper *(Cinclus cinclus)*   *Regular breeding bird*
This is a familiar bird throughout the county on most river systems, occurring on near-estuarine habitat to mountain streams at an altitude of 2,000 ft. plus.

Severe winter conditions will move birds from their inland sites to estuarine and coastal habitats as well as the larger lake shores.

Nesting takes place early in the year and holes under bridges, in hollow trees and river banks are preferred. A domed nest of moss is built. Pairs have been noted nest-building as early as February at low-level sites.

Wren *(Troglodytes troglodytes)*   *Resident*
The Wren is a common bird found in most regions of the county from the coast to high fell-sides. The population has fluctuated during the period with numbers greatly reduced during the two severe winters of 1968 and 1979. However good breeding success following these winters brought the population up to average numbers.

In winter it can be found in various habitats searching for food from inside buildings, along saltmarsh creeks and along the shoreline of upland lakes and tarns.

Dunnock *(Prunella modularis)*   *Resident*
The Dunnock is a widespread and numerous bird throughout the county. It is common in both open countryside and urban sites.

It is a pioneer species, often being the first to re-colonize coppiced woodland and the low trimmed hedgerows of modern farm management. Occasionally, birds can be found on exposed sites like fellsides and coastal headlands.

There is no recorded reference to change in status or range in the county as ringed birds usually remain fairly sedentary, although numbers recorded at Walney Bird Observatory show a marked increase during September and October.

Robin *(Erithacus rubecula)*   *Resident and passage migrant*
Widespread in open country, woodland and in urban sites. It is pugnacious to its own kind and other birds, especially from August to mid-Winter, when individuals of each sex will occupy and defend separate territories.

Although many birds remain in their breeding areas all

year, a notable Autumn passage takes place throughout the county. This is observed each year at Walney Bird Observatory where peak numbers pass through during October. A high peak of *seventy-five,* 16 Sep, 1984 at this site is exceptional.

Nightingale *(Luscinia megarhynchos)*   *Rare summer migrant*
Only two records of this notable songster have been found in the county. A bird heard singing near Millom on 26 Jul, 1956 (Field Naturalist, Vol 1, No 4) with another bird singing for a few days at Millwood, Barrow-in-Furness from 16-19 May, 1972, recorded by K Brown (LBR, No 64).

Bluethroat *(Luscinia svecica)*   *Rare passage migrant*
This handsome, Robin-like bird from Northern Europe, has only appeared four times in the county.

Stokoe's BLC refers to a male of the white-spotted race occurring at Rockcliffe on 15 Apr, 1938. The other three records are of the red-spotted race, with *one* appearing in a potato patch in an urban garden in Workington on 24 May, 1982 (G Burt *per* J C Callion). The other two were part of a large influx of birds to the north-east coast in the Spring of 1985, with *one* at Workington on 15 May and *one* on Foulney Island on 17 May.

Black Redstart *(Phoenicurus ochruros)*   *Scarce passage and winter visitor*
This is a passage migrant which occurs not far from the coast during the Autumn, Winter and early Spring months. Birds sometimes linger in suitable sites for several weeks and are regularly found on industrial sites, areas of derelict buildings, gravel pits and rubbish tips.

During the winter of 1982/3, several birds over-wintered throughout the county, including a *male* well inland at Wet Sleddale Dam, Shap Fells, which stayed through December and January (Birds in Cumbria, Spring 1983).

Another recent interesting record is of a singing *male* on 25 May, 1981 at Pendragon Castle, Mallerstang (J & K Shotton).

Redstart *(Phoenicurus phoenicurus)*   *Breeding summer visitor and passage migrant*
The Redstart is a regular breeding summer migrant of open deciduous woodland occurring on fell-sides up to the tree limit. It is scarce near the coast.

During the period under review, numbers have decreased from the population recorded in the 1960's and are now absent from several known breeding sites, particularly in the southern fells.

Passage birds usually arrive in mid-April and the return passage is complete by October. A very late *migrant* was found in Furness on 2 Dec, 1978 at Spark Bridge by D Satterthwaite. Overseas ringing recoveries include a nestling ringed near Kendal, found in north Spain three months later. A recent quick passage movement was a bird ringed at Walney Bird Observatory on 31 Aug, 1982 which was recovered dead in Madrid, Spain on 23 Sep, 1982, 1515 km.

Whinchat *(Saxicola rubetra)*   *Breeding summer visitor and passage migrant*

The population of the Whinchat has remained fairly constant throughout the period. It is an irregulary distributed bird of rough grassland and open fell-sides.

Although there is not usually an obvious passage movement, most birds arrive in late April/early May. The return passage occurs during September, with an odd late bird remaining into October. Two November records in 1981 refer to *two* birds on the 3rd at North Walney (L H Sanderson) and another on the 8th at Siddick Pond, Workington, seen by J C Callion.

Walney Bird Observatory has ringed *one hundred and seventy-four* Whinchats to date. A juvenile ringed there on 25 Aug, 1980 was caught and killed on 10 Apr, 1983 in Berrechid, Morocco, a distance of 2333 km. Other Cumbrian ringed birds have been recovered in France and Portugal.

Stonechat *(Saxicola torquata)*   *Breeding resident and passage migrant*

A very local bird with numbers varying according to the severity of the winter months. It is fairly common along the coast from Walney Island to the Solway, particularly in areas of gorse *(Ulex europea)*. It is less common on estuarine sites and in recent years has become quite scarce inland. This is most noticeable on fell-sides where they were once common twenty years ago.

Passage birds are seen in Spring, Autumn and during periods of hard weather during the Winter. These hard weather movements occasionally bring birds into unusual places, like *three* birds found on 28 Jan, 1984 at 2,000 ft. on Blencathra (G Horne).

Isabelline Wheatear *(Oenanthe isabellina)*   *Vagrant*

A bird shot at Aigle Gill, Allonby, by Thomas Mann on 11 Nov, 1887, was the first record for the British Isles of this vagrant from south east Russia, a full description of which can be found in Macpherson (VFL, p 92).

Wheatear *(Oenanthe oenanthe)*   *Breeding summer visitor and*
passage migrant

The Wheatear is a common bird in Cumbria, being found on most of the remoter upland areas up to 2,500 ft. It also occurs in lowland regions, particularly where rabbits and sheep have maintained a short turf by constant grazing. Care must be taken on a description of the bird as the local Cumbrian name for it is 'stane-chat'.

It is one of the first migrants to arrive in the Spring with birds arriving in March and invariably the last to leave in October. A very early bird arrived at Walney Bird Observatory on 24 Feb, 1984, a year which saw a late bird there on 11 Nov, but these dates are exceptional.

During the migration period large groups of birds can be found in suitable sites, such as large ploughed coastal fields, reservoir and lake shores and estuarine saltmarshes. Heavy snowfall during late April 1981, caused a spectacular 'fall' of birds throughout the Lake District, *c two hundred and fifty* in two fields near Keswick on 24 Apr, with similar reports from Kendal, Ulverston and Ambleside recorded. An unusual record of a bird on the riverbank at Abbot Hall in the centre of Kendal was seen on 14 Aug, 1976.

The Greenland race *(O. oenanthe leuchorhoa)*, which is larger, more boldly marked and more russet in coloration, is seen in small numbers around coastal sites during May and August. A good passage of this sub-species was recorded in 1984 with Walney Bird Observatory recording *seventy* birds during the months of April, May and August, *ten* on 3 Apr. A large movement was also recorded on Kirksanton airfield of *c forty-five* on 2 May, 1984.

Ring Ousel *(Turdus torquatus)*   *Breeding summer visitor and*
passage migrant

This is a local bird being most frequent in the fell country of the Pennines, Central and Shap fells. Although it is a coastal passage bird, the first arrivals in late March are often recorded on high ground, knots and scars some distance from the sea. In the Autumn small post-breeding flocks occur, often with other Thrushes feeding on fruiting mountain plants prior to migration. During the Autumn migration, birds are occasionally seen with Redwings and Fieldfares of Scandinavian origin. An early *migrant* was recorded on 19 Feb, 1984 at Walney Bird Observatory, whilst *single* birds have been known to over-winter in 1927/28 in Longsleddale and near Ings (Westmorland) in 1935/36 and 1938/9 (BTO Guide, No 15).

Blackbird *(Turdus merula)*   *Breeding resident and passage migrant*

A common bird throughout the county occurring from sea-level to around 2,000 ft. where it often overlaps with the Ring Ousel.

Many young and some adults of the local breeding population migrate both south and west during the Autumn and winter when peak inland and coastal passage can be heavy. This is recorded annually at Walney Bird Observatory in October and November where *five hundred and twenty-seven* were seen during November 1983, with *two hundred* on the 4th, although these figures are above average. At this time of year, the influx of continental birds adds to the total.

Cumbrian ringed birds have been recovered in Ireland, France, Holland, Denmark, Germany, Sweden and Norway, with the furthest recent recovery being an adult male caught at Flimby, near Maryport on 11 Feb, 1984, being recovered dead on 12 Jul, 1984 at Turki-Pori, Finland, a distance of 1673 km.

Fieldfare *(Turdus pilaris)*   *Winter visitor and passage migrant*

The first substantial flocks of Fieldfares arrive during October, when they can be found amongst fruiting hedgerows and trees, orchards and open countryside. Early migrants have been recorded in August usually involving *single* birds. *One* was found feeding on Rowan *(Sorbus aucaparia)* in Kendal on 27-29 Jul, 1982 *(per* J C Callion).

Large flocks have been seen during severe conditions in the Winter, moving south and west. A spectacular winter movement was seen along a green coastal strip, in conditions of heavy snow, in the west of the county during the last week of January 1984, when many thousands of birds passed south-westwards along the coast from Grune Point to Walney Island.

In Britain the first breeding *pair* of fieldfares was recorded in 1967, since when scattered breeding records have come from

Eastern Scotland and the Pennines as far south as Derbyshire. In Cumbria the first breeding *pair* was located on 14 Jul, 1977 in the south of the county (R Freethy). A *pair* of birds were seen feeding young in a bush on the edge of woodland near a lake.

Large wandering flocks are seen on upland countryside during March before returning to Scandinavia and Northern Europe. Late birds linger into early May with a very late bird being seen on 30 May, 1981 at Churnsike, Upper Irthing (L A Laidler).

An orange-buff leucistic bird was seen 19-24 Apr, 1978 on Sizergh Fell amongst a large party of migrant birds.

Song Thrush *(Turdus philomelos) Breeding resident and passage migrant*

The Song Thrush is a widespread breeding bird throughout the county, although it is not so common on fell-side, moorland and uncultivated areas. The population varies according to the severity of the winter months, when most local birds migrate south and west, leaving only a few birds on sites near the coast.

Winter migration is noted on Walney Bird Observatory between November and February with *one hundred and ten* on 14 Dec, 1981 and *one hundred* on 4 Nov, 1984 being peak figures.

Cumbrian ringed birds have been recovered in Ireland, France and Spain as part of a southwards movement, whereas the only return birds recovered were a bird ringed on 4 Dec, 1977 at High Harrington, Workington which was found dead on 29th Apr, 1978 at Jylland, Denmark along with another unfortunate bird which was ringed at Walney Bird Observatory on 7 Apr, 1982 and was recovered dead on 21 Apr, 1983 on the Forties Delta Oil Rig in the North Sea. This bird was dazzled by the lights and burnt in the 'burn-off' flame.

Redwing *(Turdus iliacus)*   *Winter visitor and passage migrant*

The Redwing usually arrives in large parties in late September, a few weeks before the Fieldfare appears in any large quantity. Like their larger counterpart, they can be found feeding in fruiting trees and hedgerows and in orchards. Most Autumn passage is nocturnal with birds moving on clear frosty nights when they can be heard communicating with their single-syllable calls. On occasions a heavy passage movement is seen in daylight, such as *c ten thousand* moving south on 16 Oct, 1982 over Cold Fell in the Northern Pennines (J Miles). Most birds move south and west through the county, leaving smaller parties to winter in the region.

Numbers start to build up again by mid-March as birds gather for the return migration. Many birds gather in open woodland where some can be heard singing their fluty sub-song. Most birds have gone by mid-April, with only the odd singing bird remaining into May over the last twenty years. A few summer records in the period include; *two,* 10 Jul, 1971 at Burneside (A Whiteside); *one,* all summer 1975 at High Harrington, Workington; a *male* singing on 1 Jun, 1980 in Upper Irthing, Northern Pennines (J Holland); a bird found dead on 19 Jul, 1982 at Castle Head, Grange-over-Sands (T H Jorgensen).

A leucistic bird was found near Whinfell Tarn, near Kendal on 12 Dec, 1976 by R Nichol and M Hutcheson. The bird was buff to cream in colour, with a paler eye-stripe and orange patches under the wings.

Ringing in the county has proved this bird to be a long distance traveller. Some of the more notable returns being; a bird ringed on 16 Dec, 1967 at Broughton-in-Furness, recovered on 5 Mar, 1970 at Preveza, Greece (2340 km.); a bird ringed at Barrow on 20 Feb, 1967, recovered 8 Jun, 1969 in Georgia, USSR (2250 km.), with another ringed at Walney Bird Observatory on 3 Mar, 1979, found dead on 28 Jun, 1979 at Arkangelsk, USSR (2689 km.).

Mistle Thrush *(Turdus viscivorus)*   *Breeding resident and passage migrant*

This is a bird of the woodland edge, open parkland and suburban parks and gardens, with breeding pairs being found up to 1,500 ft. It is an early nesting bird and many pairs are predated by Magpies and Jays, even though parent birds prove to be very aggressive.

Post-breeding flocks of up to *fifty* birds can be found roaming fellsides and open fields, before they migrate south. This occurs during July and August and are often confused for early flocks of Fieldfares.

A nest was found containing eggs during December 1984 on a support of a pipe system at Glaxo factory, Ulverston (D Jewel). *Three* fledglings were seen on 4 Jan, 1985.

Coastal passage movement is noted during periods of severe weather in the winter.

American Robin *(Turdus migratorius)*   *Vagrant*

A bird of this species stayed around the garden of a house at Brampton, near Carlisle from 2-6 Mar, 1955 and was watched regularly by Miss C L Murray and Miss K S Hodgson. It remains underlined as it has not been submitted to the BBRC but is recorded by Stokoe BLC.

Grasshopper Warbler *(Locustella naevia)*   *Breeding visitor and passage migrant*

This is a summer visitor which can be found in marshland, reed-beds and coastal mosses. It is local in its distribution and variable in numbers, never being a common bird, but regular in favoured habitat.

Spring arrivals usual appear in late April, with the return passage occurring in September. Small numbers move through Walney Bird Observatory each year, with most birds occurring in May. To date, *thirty-five* birds have been ringed here, with as yet no returns.

Savi's Warbler *(Locustella luscinioides)*   *Very rare migrant*

The first and only record to date of this warbler, occurred on a coastal marsh in 1982. The bird was heard singing on several occasions from 6 Apr to 17 Jun (Observers names withheld).

Sedge Warbler *(Acrocephalus schoenabaenus)* *Breeding summer visitor, passage migrant*

This is a common summer visitor to suitable habitat, which includes reed-beds and thick vegetation on damp ground or near water. Sometimes birds are found in non-aquatic sites during Spring passage, such as a singing bird in a blackthorn thicket on the M6 motorway embankment, 14 May, 1983, at Beck Foot, Dillicar in the Lune Valley.

The first migrant birds arrive in mid-April and the last birds are usually seen in September. A bird ringed on 13 Sep, 1974 at Ile du Migron, Loire Atlantique, France was recovered on 27 May, 1975 at Walney Bird Observatory.

Paddyfield Warbler *(Acrocephalus agricola)*   *Vagrant*

A first year bird at Walney Bird Observatory, 11-13 Sep, 1982, was trapped and ringed on the 11th. This is the first county record and only the eighth in the British Isles (T Dean, K Parkes *et al*). Full account in WBO Report for 1982.

PaddyField Warbler.

Reed Warbler *(Acrocephalus scirpaceus)*   *Scarce breeding summer migrant*

Although Cumbria represents the furthest point north this Warbler has attempted to breed, records during the period under review suggest it is becoming better established and spreading slowly northwards. It favours lakes, tarns and water courses where there is a good growth of Reed *(Phragmites communis)* and now breeds regularly in several such sites in the south of the county. Birds reached two north western sites near the coast in 1980, where they too have become established.

Birds normally arrive in mid-April and their song can be heard well into June. Most birds have left by September.

A *female* caught and ringed on 23 Jul, 1983 on Lower Test Marsh, Totton, Hants was recovered on 8 Jul, 1984 at Helton Tarn, Witherslack. This is a very interesting recovery indicating a breeding female which moved from one of the most southerly sites to one of the most north westerly locations.

Icterine Warbler *(Hippolais icterina)*   *Very rare migrant*

Only three records of this perky stout Warbler, which breeds in Northern Europe, have occurred in the county. All of them were trapped and ringed in mid-August at Walney Bird Observatory and were recorded on 23 Aug, 1977, 19 Aug, 1983 and 23 Aug, 1984.

Melodious Warbler *(Hippolais polyglotta)*   *Rare passage migrant*

The Melodious Warbler is very similar to the Icterine Warbler, except that it breeds in Southern Europe. It is a little surprising therefore to find that it has occurred no less than twelve times during the period under review.

With the awareness of Warbler passage along the coast, Walney Bird Observatory has so far had eleven records of this bird of which eight were trapped and ringed. *Six* appeared in August, *three* in September with *singles* in May and June.

A *single* bird was also identified in Ranleigh Park, Barrow-in-Furness on 3 Sep, 1981 by A Phizacklea.

Barred Warbler *(Sylvia nisoria)*   *Rare passage migrant*

Stokoe's BLC relates the first record of this bird which he trapped and ringed at Grune Point on the Solway on 6 Sep, 1959. Since that date a further eleven records have occurred in the period under review. *Four* trapped and ringed at Grune Point during September (G Horne *et al*) and *six* at Walney Bird Observatory during August and September. A bird was also recorded at Siddick Pond, Workington on 21 Aug, 1977 (J C Callion). All records were of immature or first year birds.

Lesser Whitethroat *(Sylvia curruca)*   *Scarce breeding bird and passage migrant*

This is a scarce breeding bird in the county which has a few favoured localities where it returns with regularity each year. Although a sparse breeding bird it has been recorded more often in the lower valley areas of the Kent and the Duddon as well as on the Solway Plain. Some increase in breeding sites have been recorded since 1970 onwards, particularly in the north of the county.

It is a bird of copse, coppice woodland, hedgerow and waste ground where hawthorn dominates. It is also found in parkland and mature dune slacks where shrub growth is fairly mature.

The first migrants usually appear in May and most have departed by the end of August. An early *migrant* was found at Carr Beds, Rockcliffe on 18 Apr, 1981.

Whitethroat *(Sylvia communis)*   *Summer passage migrant and breeding bird*

The dramatic decrease of the Whitethroat population in 1969 in Britain is well documented by the BTO in their 'Atlas', in which information from the Common Bird Census shows

77% of the previous year's breeding stock failed to reappear. In Cumbria, numbers did decline though not as drastically as in some other regions. Populations remain fairly constant around the Cumbrian coast, on the Solway Plain and in some of the South Lakeland valleys. Although they seem to be variable in numbers each year, they are slowly increasing to their former status.

The first migrants appear in April, with most of them having left by October. An odd winter record of a bird at Flimby, near Maryport on 13 Dec, 1974 was seen by Miss M Milne.

Good numbers of Whitethroat have been trapped and ringed in Cumbria over the last twenty years, with *seven hundred and forty* alone at Walney Bird Observatory. From these marked birds recoveries have come from both Portugal and Spain.

Garden Warbler *(Sylvia borin)*   *Summer passage migrant and breeding bird*

The Garden Warbler is not quite like any other British species in that it lacks in any prominent features. It breeds in areas of waste ground where there is suitable cover, large gardens, parkland and road and railway embankments.

It is not a common bird in Cumbria, yet is fairly widespread in small numbers, except in the Central Fells area where it is scarce.

Spring migrants usually arrive in May and most have departed by September. A bird seen amongst migrant Thrushes and Finches in the yews on Helsington Barrows, Kendal on 12 Oct, 1985 was a late bird (A F Gould).

A Garden Warbler which was trapped and ringed on 23 Jul, 1983 at Longtown, was found dead on 24 Nov, 1983 at Kumasi, Ghana, 5370 km. This was the first recovery south of the Sahara of a British ringed Garden Warbler.

Blackcap *(Sylvia atricapilla)*   *Passage migrant and breeding bird*

This is a regular bird of woodland, gardens, orchards and scrub areas where there is cover, the most favoured sites being the edge of mature deciduous woodland.

Stokoe's BLC quotes this bird as 'being less numerous than the Garden Warbler during the first part of the century', though numbers certainly outweigh the Garden Warbler population to date.

Over the past decade there is a trend for an increasing number of Blackcaps to winter in the region, especially near coast and estuarine sites. These birds are often quite bold as they frequently visit bird-tables where they have been seen to feed on apples, peanuts, raisins and other fruit. Ringing recoveries have proved that some of these birds are of Scandinavian origin, which suggests that some of that population replaces our breeding population in the Autumn. A bird trapped and ringed on 7 Oct, 1981 on Fair Isle, Scotland was retrapped on 28 Dec, 1981 at Barrow.

Pallas's Warbler *(Phylloscopus proregulus)*   *Vagrant*
Two specimens of this little green Siberian 'gem' were seen and photographed on South Walney on 13 Oct, 1983 (T Dean, L H Sanderson *et al*). They were the first record for the county and were accepted by the BBRC.

They were part of an unprecedented influx of Pallas's Warblers to Britain, when no less than *one hundred and twenty-seven* birds were recorded. Prior to this, the highest total recorded in any year in Britain was *thirty-three* in 1981, which at the time was thought to be exceptional for a bird which normally occurs rarely (British Birds 78: 381-392, Aug, 1985).

Yellow-browed Warbler *(Phylloscopus inornatus)*   *Rare migrant visitor*
Stokoe's BLC records a *single* bird on 14 Oct, 1920 at the Waver Estuary. Since that date a further *eight* records of this Siberian warbler have been recorded in the county. This is in common with the general trend for this species, as a sudden upsurge of records has occurred in Britain and Ireland since the late 1960's. The Cumbrian records include:

> *One,* 5 Oct, 1968, Walney Bird Observatory, trapped and ringed.
> *One,* 20 Oct, 1979, Longtown (J C Callion) — seen with Goldcrests.
> *One,* 3 Oct, 1981, Walney Bird Observatory, trapped and ringed.
> *One,* 17 Oct, 1981, Grune Point, Solway (G Horne, R C Shaw, I Armstrong), trapped and ringed.
> *One,* 8-9 Nov, 1982, Walney Bird Observatory. The plumage and other characteristics of this bird suggested it to be of the race *Ph. inornatus humei,* which comes from Eastern Europe (T Dean).
> *One,* 26 Sep, 1985, Walney Bird Observatory.
> *Two,* 18 Oct, 1985, Walney Bird Observatory, one of these birds was trapped and ringed.

Bonelli's Warbler.

S.L.

Bonelli's Warbler *(Phylloscopus bonelli)*   *Vagrant*
The first record for the county of this warbler, which breeds in central and southern Europe, occurred on 7 May, 1984 on North Walney (S Lawson, L H Sanderson *et al*). This rare leaf warbler was first identified by its song and later was seen with difficulty as it is a bird of the upper foliage, being very active and agile. It was accepted by BBRC.

Wood Warbler *(Phylloscopus sibilatrix)*   *Summer passage migrant and breeding bird*
The Wood Warbler is a bird of mature deciduous woodland with a good area of undergrowth for cover.

It usually arrives in late April and departs in August. It is fairly common in some of the woods of the lake shores and valleys of the central and northern Lake District area. It is infrequent in the more agricultural areas around the coast and in the Solway Plain. As a passage migrant it seems to keep to woodland associated with the various river systems in the county, following them upstream. It is rarely recorded along the coastline, a fact which is borne out at Walney Bird Observatory where they trapped and ringed a bird on 5 Sep, 1982, the only record there in twenty years.

Chiffchaff *(Phylloscopus collybita)*   *Passage migrant and breeding bird*
This is a local migrant which is thinly distributed in the county in areas of mixed woodland with thick undergrowth. It is an uncommon bird in the eastern part of the county and is recorded mainly as a passage migrant in the Eden Valley and in the Pennine foothill woodlands.

It arrives in late March and departs in September. It is occasionally found in October and records of birds over-wintering are increasing.

A bird of the race *Ph. collybita tristis* was trapped and ringed on 25 Dec, 1956 at Stainton, near Kendal by J W Allen.

Willow Warbler *(Phylloscopus trochilus)*   *Passage migrant and breeding bird*

The Willow Warbler is a common breeding bird throughout the county. It favours a wooded or semi-wooded breeding site in a wide range of habitat from deciduous woodland, parkland, hedgerows, embankments with willow and scrub cover and large gardens. In the Lakeland valleys it can occur up to around 1,000 ft.

It arrives with regularity during the first weeks of April, departing in September. Contrary to this, a very early bird was found at Askam-in-Furness on 12 Mar, 1978 by R Freethy. There are also two November records in the period under review. A bird found at Low Sizergh on 3 Nov, 1980 (M Burnside) was found to have a damaged eye, while a bird on 8 Nov, 1982, was the last of four November records that year at Walney Bird Observatory.

Passage can be heavy in some years with a notable passage being recorded at Walney Bird Observatory during Aug, 1983. Here, *seventy* birds were recorded on both 17 and 22 Aug, with a total of *four hundred and forty-three* birds for the whole month. Birds ringed at Walney Bird Observatory have been recovered in both France and Portugal.

Other interesting recoveries elsewhere in the county include a bird ringed on 15 Apr, 1984 at West Vlanderen, Belgium which was recovered at Penrith on 5 Aug, 1984. Even more remarkable was a bird ringed on 20 Apr, 1984 at Watchet, Somerset, which was recovered on North Walney the next day, a distance of 330 km. This was a very fast passage movement.

A leucistic bird was found on 10 Jun, 1982 on the Smardale Nature Reserve by R & D Baines who described it as having the plumage of a day old chick, with an orange back and legs and red eyes.

Goldcrest *(Regulus regulus)*   *Passage migrant and breeding bird*

This is a common breeding bird in both mixed and coniferous woodland and can often be found in suitable habitat on wooded fellsides up to 1,500 ft. The outer branches of a conifer is the usual nest-site for this bird, but they have been known to nest in gorse.

Passage movement occurs in March, April, September and October with smaller numbers moving in the winter months during severe weather conditions. Exceptional numbers occurred during 1983 at Walney Bird Observatory where peak figures were *two hundred* on 6 Apr, *two hundred and fifty* on 10 Sep and *three hundred and fifty* on 7 Oct. *Three hundred and seven* birds were ringed that year out of a total of *nine hundred and eighty-eight* ringed since the Observatory started in 1964. A bird ringed there on 2 Oct, 1983 was found dead on 1 Nov, 1983 at Le Porge, Gironde, France, a total of 1032 km.

Firecrest *(Regulus ignicapillus)*   *Scarce passage migrant*
The Firecrest has within the period under review become an established breeding bird in a few of the southern counties of England. As a consequence this has increased the number of records in Cumbria in recent years. One or two birds are recorded annually during the months of passage, namely April to June and October to December. An occasional bird has over-wintered.

Spotted Flycatcher *(Muscicapa striata)*   *Passage migrant and breeding bird*
This is a regular breeding bird throughout the county and is one of the last summer migrants to arrive in Spring. The first birds appear in early May and are quick to take up territories in open woodland, parkland or gardens. The first eggs are often laid within a fortnight of their arrival.

A normal pattern is for two broods to be reared, with family parties mixing with other warblers in small groups prior to the start of the return migration in August. Most birds have departed by late September.

Ringing returns have proved the Spotted Flycatcher to be a long distance traveller, with a bird ringed on 13 Aug, 1966 at Walney Bird Observatory being recovered on 4 Oct, 1966 at Enugu, Nigeria. This, at the time, was the first recovery south of the Sahara.

Red-breasted Flycatcher *(Ficedula parva)*   *Rare passage migrant*
This bird is a rare passage migrant in Cumbria, even though it is recorded annually on the east coast of Britain. The first record was of a *male* seen in a wood on the south-east side of

Loughrigg Fell near Ambleside on 10 Sep, 1946 (British Birds 40; p 84) by Barbara J Bird. Only four more records have been added to this to date, all of them at Walney Bird Observatory. They are; an *immature,* 1 Oct, 1972, trapped and ringed; a *juvenile,* 14 Oct, 1974; an *immature male,* 14 Oct, 1977, trapped and ringed and an *adult,* 8 Jun, 1984.

Pied Flycatcher *(Ficedula hypoleuca)*   *Passage migrant and breeding bird*

The Pied Flycatcher is a locally common summer visitor to open deciduous woodland and parkland, being more frequent where oak is dominant. It arrives in mid-April with breeding birds often leaving their nest sites by July. Migration is mainly coastal and continues through August, when it is most noticeable, into September.

With the nest-site usually being a hole in a tree, the policy of 'clean' forestry in the region is allowed for by several conservation groups erecting nest boxes. One such scheme in the Grizedale Forest has around two hundred boxes involved in it.

Recent local study and ringing at these sites has proved that breeding pairs do not always return to the same site each year. A *breeding female* in Kentmere in 1979 was found in a nest-box in Noord Ginkel, Holland, the following year (S T Robinson).

Several Cumbrian bred Pied Flycatchers have been recovered in Europe, particularly in Spain. The longest distance recovery to date was a bird ringed 20 Jun, 1970 in Grizedale Forest which was recovered on 20 Apr 1971 at Yamani, Morocco, a distance of 2120 km.

Bearded Tit *(Panurus biarmicus)*

Last recorded as a breeding bird two centuries ago, the Bearded Tit has never been able to re-establish itself in the county. This has made the 'irruption' movement of *four* birds seen on 30 Oct, 1978 at Elterwater (Miss M Arnette and Mrs M Thacker) and a party of *fifteen* on 6-7 Nov, 1981 at Siddick Pond, Workington (J C Callion) an interesting development.

Long-tailed Tit *(Aegithalos caudatus)*   *Resident breeding bird*

This is a bird of woodland, hedgerows, thickets and gardens. It is fairly widespread as a breeding species and has been recorded up to 1,000 ft. on some wooded fell-sides.

Its nest of moss, lichen and feathers is most delicate and attractive and is sited in a hawthorn, gorse or thorny thicket or the upper branches of spruce in forestry plantations.

In winter, flocks of these birds associate with other Titmice, Treecreepers and Goldcrest, roaming along hedgerows for food.

No obvious migration of this species has been recorded in the county, although Stokoe's BLC refers to the Continental white-headed race as being seen in 1891.

Marsh Tit *(Parus palustris)*   *Resident breeding bird*
This is a local resident which is found in the southern half of the county in the 'old' counties of Furness and Westmorland. Further north it becomes scarce with only a few records coming from the Northern Lakes area, the Eden Valley and along the Northern Pennines. A record of *five* on 5 Dec, 1981 at Bewcastle is unusual (CBR 1981).

Willow Tit *(Parus montanus)*   *Resident breeding bird*
The reverse can be said about the Willow Tit in comparison with the status of the Marsh Tit. It is most frequent in the damp woodlands and mosses of the west coast and the Solway Plain. It also occurs in the Northern Lakes area but is sporadic and very local elsewhere in the county.

It favours damp boggy woodland, especially with areas of Alder and Birch which are used as nest sites.

Crested Tit *(Parus cristatus)*   *Rare visitor*
A bird found in a mixed party of Tits on 16 Feb, 1954 by Mrs E J Wilson at the head of Derwentwater must be regarded as genuine, as the bird was seen at close range by this eminent naturalist for around five minutes.

The origin of this bird is an intriguing question as the Crested Tit is a regular breeding bird on the Continent from Southern Spain through France to Scandinavia, as well as the British population in the Scottish Highlands. This bird could have come from either source.

Coal Tit *(Parus ater)*   *Resident breeding bird*
The population of the Coal Tit has increased in the period under review as it now is a regular bird of coniferous woodland throughout the county and can be found up to 1,500 ft. in the higher Lakeland valleys.

During the winter months it wanders away from its breeding haunts and can be found in mixed flocks of tits foraging in hedgerows and in gardens.

Stokoe's BLC refers to passage birds of the Irish race *(Parus ater hibernicus)* being seen on the Solway in 1961, but no further records have come to light since then.

Blue Tit *(Parus caeruleus)*   *Resident breeding bird*
This is a common bird throughout the county especially in suitable habitat with open woodland, parkland, hedgerows and gardens.

In winter birds are often found in flocks of other species, like Finches, foraging for seed. At this time they can often be found around the edges of lakes and tarns feeding in reed-beds.

The Blue Tit is fairly sedentary so the following recoveries are of interest. A bird ringed on 6 Nov, 1981 at Low Hauxley, Northumberland was recovered on 21 Jan, 1982 in Carlisle. Another interesting movement was a bird ringed on 3 Oct, 1981 at Walney Bird Observatory and recovered twice at Bispham, Blackpool on 26 Oct, 1981 and 4 Mar, 1982, then surprisingly on 24 Mar, 1984, at Lakeside, Windermere.

Great Tit *(Parus major)*   *Resident breeding bird*
Like the Blue Tit, the Great Tit is widespread throughout the county, in similar habitat. They both are found in close association with man in towns and villages, being regular visitors to bird-tables.

In common with other members of the tit family, their breeding sites are vacated during the winter months and they move about the countryside in small parties looking for food. They also seem to be fairly sedentary as no outstanding movements have been recorded in the county, the only one of note being a bird ringed on 18 Jun, 1982 at Greenhaugh, Northumberland, which was recovered on 12 Feb, 1983 near Maryport, suggesting that a movement may occur to the milder west coast in winter.

Nuthatch *(Sitta europaea)*   *Local resident breeding bird*
The Nuthatch is slowly increasing its range in a positive manner in Cumbria, in the period under review. Over the last ten years it has spread from its stronghold around Lake Windermere and Coniston Water. *Pairs* have been found in Levens Park and Grange-over-Sands in the south, Sedbergh in the east, Eskdale and Muncaster in the west and Borrowdale and Keswick in the north, with single birds being recorded in 1984 in the Border area and in the Northern Pennine valleys. Single birds are often found in Winter with mixed parties of Tits.

Treecreeper *(Certhia familiaris)*   *Resident breeding bird*
This bird is found in most woodland habitat, including both coniferous and deciduous trees. It is also found in open sites

where there are mature trees like parkland, hedgerows and gardens.

The habit of the Treecreeper making a small recess in the soft bark of the American Big Tree *(Wellingtonia gigantea)* for a roost site is well documented. This habit has been recorded in many parkland areas in the county, along with roost-sites in the hollows in the trunks of mature Yew *(Taxus baccata).* Communal roosting, involving four or five birds at these sites has also been recorded.

During the Winter small numbers of birds can be found foraging with mixed parties of Tits, Goldcrest, etc. and can be found away from mature trees at this time.

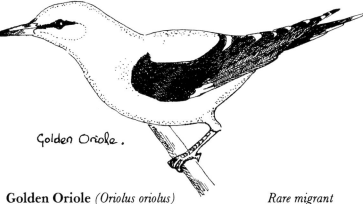

Golden Oriole.

Golden Oriole *(Oriolus oriolus)*   *Rare migrant*
The Golden Oriole has been recorded in the county between the months of April and August, with most records occurring in May.

Stokoe's BLC relates to eleven records prior to 1958 and to the event of a pair which bred in the Rusland Valley in 1958 and 1959 (J A G Barnes, L Cowcill) and to the appearance of a pair at this site in 1960 and 1961. Records since that date include;

Pair, 8 Jul-14 Aug, 1965, Wet Sleddale Dam (J M White) (Field Naturalist, Vol 11, No 3).

Male, 16 Aug, 1966, Borrowdale, Keswick (Field Naturalist, Vol 11, No 4).

Male, 19 May, 1967, Barrow-in-Furness (K Brown).

Male, 16 Apr, 1974, Torver (J Wilcox) — a very early migrant.

Immature male, 6 Jun, 1975, Docker Wood, near Kendal (A F Gould).

Male, 16-18 Jun, 1980, Seatoller Bridge (Mrs D Davies).

Female, 14 Jun, 1981, Grune Point, Solway (Mr & Mrs R Spencer).

Immature male, 19 and 30 May, 1983, North Walney (T Dean, L H Sanderson).

Male, 29 May, 1983, Holker Park, Cartmel (Miss V Amor).

Male, 24 May, 1984, Longsleddale (A F Gould).

Red-backed Shrike *(Lanius collurio)*   *Rare migrant*

This was a scarce breeding bird in the eighteenth century. Now it is a rare passage bird, with only eight records in the period under review. Oddly, Stokoe's BLC has no records between 1935 and 1964. Records to date include;

Male, 24 Mar-7 Apr, 1968, Aspatria (H N Hammond).

Male, 7 Jun, 1969, Little Mell Fell (J H White).

Female, 17 Jun, 1974, Allonby (Mrs S Richardson).

Male, 7 Jul, 1974, St Bees Head (M Blackburn).

Pair, 25 May, 1977, Crummock Water (H Goodman).

Male, 7 Jul, 1979, Howtown, Martindale (Mrs J B Nicholas).

Female, 25 May, 1983, North Walney (C Johnston).

Male, 10 Jun, 1983, Grune Point, Solway (R & M A Spencer).

Great Grey Shrike *(Lanius excubitor)*   *Irregular winter visitor*

The Great Grey Shrike is an irregular winter visitor from Scandinavia. Single birds will appear in an open locality, often near water, where they will sometimes remain all winter.

It is often recognised from a distance, as it will regularly perch at the top of a tree or telegraph pole where it watches for suitable prey. This includes large insects, small mammals and birds. Records occur between late October and April.

Woodchat Shrike *(Lanius senator)*   *Vagrant*

Stokoe's BLC quotes an old record at Workington in April 1872.

A fine *adult* bird was found near Walney airfield, where it remained from 2-7 Jun, 1984 (K Parkes, A Lawton *et al*). The record was accepted by the BBRC.

Jay *(Garrulus glandarius)*   *Resident breeding bird*

The Jay is a locally common woodland bird which prefers mixed deciduous woods and can occur up to 1,000 ft. in the Central Fells.

Local movements of small parties of birds occur in late

Autumn and Winter when they move from one area of oak to another, acorns being a favourite diet. These small flocks can hold a dozen or so birds.

An unusual migration into Britain from Europe occurred in the Autumn 1983, when small flocks of Jays appeared in arable areas, such as the Solway Plain, along the coastal strip and in Furness. *sixteen* → S on 28 Sep, at Sizergh Castle being the largest flock recorded.

Woodchat Shrike

SL.

Magpie *(Pica pica)*   *Resident breeding bird*
Even though this bird is common throughout most of the county, with its population still increasing, it always has been and still is scarce along the Pennine foothills and in the Eden Valley. Some of the increase may be due to the reduction in game-keeping and the fact that the bird is not persecuted as much. This in turn may be the reason why it is becoming less timid with birds being found more often in parks and gardens in the centres of our larger towns.

Nest-sites are usually well chosen in thick Hawthorn hedge, or concealed in conifer, Holly or other evergreen or near the top of a large tree.

Winter roosts containing large numbers of birds are well known. A site with *sixty-six* birds in it was recorded in Kentmere in November 1981.

Migrational movements are not often recorded as few Magpies have been ringed. A bird ringed on 26 May, 1982 at Walney Bird Observatory was recovered at Little Bispham, Blackpool on 31 Jul, 1983.

Nutcracker *(Nucifraga caryocatactes)*   *Vagrant*

Only two records of this rare Corvid from Northern Europe have occurred in Cumbria, both of them in the last twenty years.

> *One,* 22 Oct, 1978, Fallbarrow Park, Bowness-on-Windermere (R J Faunt)
> *One,* 1 Dec, 1979, Walney Bird Observatory (T Dean *et al*).

Both records were accepted by the BBRC.

Chough *(Pyrrhocorax pyrrhocorax)*   *Rare passage bird*

The Chough was last recorded as a breeding bird in Cumbria in 1870 when Macpherson's VFL states that 'two or three pairs nesting on St Bees Head until around 1860'. He also states 'the species bred on Whitbarrow, a range of limestone precipices commanding a fine view of Morecambe Bay, between 1862 and 1865'.

In more recent times the Chough has occurred in the county as a straggler with single birds or occasionally a pair and generally recorded near the coast.

Two seen on 21 Apr, 1961 on Foulney Island and a dead bird found at the same site on 22 Apr, 1968 along with a bird on 10 Jul, 1970 at Threlkeld (*per* L A Cowcill) are three previously unpublished records. Since that date a further twelve records have appeared in the Cumbria Bird Report up to 1984. Several inland records were reported including a bird found on 15 May, 1979 at Mallerstang, the first Pennine record this century (Mrs W Ellwood).

Jackdaw *(Corvus monedula)*   *Common resident breeding bird*

The Jackdaw population has increased dramatically over the last century in Cumbria. It is most common in towns and villages where it nests in old buildings and chimneys. They can also be found up to an altitude of 1,000 ft. nesting in quarries and cliff faces. They nest regularly on the coastal cliffs of St Bees.

Large communal roosts are found in winter in several parts of the county, often in association with Rooks and regularly holding *several thousand* birds.

An obvious passage southwards with other Corvids occurs at Walney Bird Observatory in late October and early November. Even so, ringed birds remain fairly sedentary except for a bird ringed on 19 Dec, 1975 in Wexford, Ireland, which was recovered on 7 Jun, 1982 near Penrith.

Rook *(Corvus frugilegus)*   *Common resident breeding bird*
This is a highly successful bird which is widespread throughout the county from the coast to fell-side, particularly in areas of intense agriculture.

Recent ornithological surveys show that the population has increased dramatically in some country areas, whereas rookeries in urban and town situations have decreased in some instances in the last ten years. Rookeries in the country areas are usually found along the main highways. Very large rookeries are a thing of the past as the 1975 BTO Rookeries survey revealed. The birds seem to be using more sites with a lesser number of nests. The largest rookery in the 1975 survey in the Westmorland and Furness area was at Acorn Bank, Temple Sowerby in the Eden Valley, which held 207 nests. this is far below the large rookery mentioned in Stokoe's BLC of 528 nests at Penny Bridge Hall in 1945.

Large winter roosts have now become established in several areas of the county, with places like Hethersgill, Hackthorpe, Dallam Towers and Levens Park holding between *a thousand* and *three thousand* birds in late 1984.

Carrion Crow *(Corvus corone corone)*   *Common resident breeding bird*
The Carrion Crow is a numerous and widespread bird which has increased in numbers quite substantially in the last fifty years. Birds have now found their way into urban situations and are regularly found scavenging in town centres like Carlisle and Barrow.

It is a tree nesting species which usually picks a secure tall tree with a good canopy of foliage for cover. Nest-sites have been found up to an altitude of 1,800 ft. where the birds are often restricted to nesting on the lower levels of a rock face or on tall shrubs.

Albino birds have been found in the county on several occasions. One bird was seen in 1971 in the Lune Valley and remained in the area for at least nine years. Others have been recorded in the Kershope Forest in 1981 and Farleton Fell, Kent Valley in 1982. A leucistic bird was found in 1979 in Eskdale and a hybrid Carrion × Hooded Crow was described in 1982 in the Ingmire district of Sedbergh.

Hooded Crow *(Corvus corone cornix)*   *Passage migrant*
Although the Hooded Crow is a sub-species of the Carrion Crow, it has been put under a separate heading here as in

Cumbria it is a definite passage bird. It is an infrequent winter visitor, occurring mainly around the coast. At Walney Bird Observatory they appear annually, some staying to feed on the shore for a few days, others noted on passage with other Corvids. These passage birds are likely to be of Manx or Irish origin. One or two birds are normally recorded with *five,* 19 Dec, 1981 being unusual.

Elsewhere, they are a rare bird, especially inland thus making *two,* 29 Oct, 1948, at Redhills, Penrith (W Atkinson); *one,* 15 Oct, 1955 at Great Asby (R Stokoe); *one,* 28 Jan-26 Mar, 1978 at Kirkby Lonsdale (R Aitken); *one,* 21 Dec, 1983 at Burneside (P A Robinson) and *one,* 6 Oct, 1984 at Hardknott Pass (D Morgan) all noteworthy.

Raven *(Corvus corax)*   *Resident breeding bird*

The Raven, although still persecuted, can be found in the mountainous regions of the county in good numbers. It breeds on crag-sides, cliff-faces and sometimes in trees at an altitude of 1,000 ft. plus. Several pairs breed on coastal cliffs.

Breeding starts early in the year with nest building often in progress during February. Despite the constant attention from a few uneducated landowners and egg-collectors, the population in Cumbria is stable.

A local movement of birds occurs in the Spring and Autumn between the Lakeland Fells and the Pennines.

Another local feature is the gathering of birds in small flocks. This has been recorded mainly in the Autumn and Winter months, but can occur at any time. Around twenty birds is the average number for one of these flocks with *forty-eight,* 17 Apr, 1981 around Wallow Crag, Haweswater being exceptional.

Starling *(Sturnus vulgaris)*   *Common breeding and passage migrant*

This is a common breeding bird throughout the county, even in the isolated valleys and fellsides where they were scarce some fifty years ago.

Numbers increase dramatically in the Autumn when post breeding flocks join the local population from Northern Europe and Scandinavia. They often come with migrant Thrushes and feed with them in the fields and on the fruits and berries in the hedgerows.

Large flocks build up at communal roost sites during the Autumn and Winter, sometimes many thousands strong. They regularly choose roost sites in city and town centres on buildings, in reed-beds on the lake shore and in conifer plantations.

Ringing has produced some interesting returns in the period under review, with *three* Cumbrian ringed recoveries from Finland and *one* each in West Germany, Denmark, Norway and Sweden. The most interesting recovery is of a bird ringed on 3 Feb, 1980 at Flimby, near Maryport, being found injured on 11 May, 1981 in Latvia, USSR.

Albinoism is not uncommon in Starlings and albino birds are often amongst the large flocks seen at the end of the year.

Rose-coloured Starling *(Sturnus roseus)*   *Vagrant*

Stokoe's BLC, 'several old records up to 1898, when a bird was seen at Allonby during that summer'.

House Sparrow *(Passer domesticus)*   *Common resident breeding bird*

The House Sparrow is an abundant species over most of Cumbria, except on the isolated farms on the Lakeland fells and in the Pennines.

Where birds do breed in upland areas they often desert these sites in winter in favour of gathering in foraging flocks at lower levels.

Albino and leucistic birds have been recorded in the period under review.

Tree Sparrow *(Passer montanus)*   *Resident breeding bird*

This is a local bird which nests in small colonies in open woodland, old farm buildings and in hedgerow trees. It is found in good numbers in arable areas, particularly on the Solway Plain, in the Eden Valley and along the Cumbrian coast. South of the Central Fells it has an irregular distribution. Young birds disperse over a wide area in the Autumn.

During the winter months, flocks of Tree Sparrows roam the hedgerows, farm yards and stubble fields looking for food along with other Finches and Buntings.

Chaffinch *(Fringilla coelebs)*   *Resident breeding bird and passage migrant*

The Chaffinch is a regular breeding bird of both urban and open countryside. It occurs in upland areas up to around 1,500 ft.

Outside the breeding season, flocks of birds can be found in areas of open woodland, especially if they include Beech

(Fagus sylvatica) and in stubble fields. Often these flocks are segregated into groups of male or female birds.

During the winter these flocks are enlarged in numbers by migrants from Northern Europe and often hold *several hundred* birds. These birds move into stack-yards and around farm buildings in severe conditions.

Coastal migration can be seen in the late Autumn, particularly during October and November when these birds are considered to be moving west into Ireland and south into Europe.

Ringing recoveries during the period include a Barrow ringed bird in Antwerp, Belgium and a Norwegian ringed bird in Carlisle.

Brambling *(Fringilla montifringilla)*   *Winter passage migrant*
This is an annual winter visitor to Cumbria, which in some years is abundant and in others it is scarce. The first birds arrive in October and are often found in small numbers with Chaffinches in stubble, kale or root fields, rickyards and in beech woodland.

In the winter period between December and February, large flocks can be found, often *several hundred* strong. These large parties are often recorded in town parks under Beech looking for 'mast'. In periods of heavy snowfall flocks will often congregate along the shoreline on the coast to feed on seed washed up on the tideline.

Most birds have gone by April, although several full plumaged males have been found in song in a few sites on occasion during the period.

Migration is noted along the coast and has been recorded on the fell-tops.

A bird ringed on 26 Dec, 1970 in Heligoland was recovered on 1 Feb, 1972 at High Nibthwaite (L A Cowcill).

Greenfinch *(Carduelis chloris)*   *Resident breeding bird and winter migrant*
This is a frequent bird of gardens, parkland, and open countryside where there is sufficient cover with scattered woodland and hedgerow. In the winter months it can be found in various habitats from stubble fields, reed-beds, saltings and coastal shoreline.

During the Winter, local roost sites in a large area of mature Rhododendron or other evergreen shrubs often hold *several hundred* birds, attracting birds from a wide district.

Although this bird is fairly sedentary in the county, there is a movement north and south during the year as recorded by local ringing schemes.

Goldfinch *(Carduelis carduelis)*   *Resident breeding bird*

The Goldfinch is a bird of the lower levels, frequenting gardens, orchards and the agricultural areas of the county. Foraging flocks may be found in Autumn and Winter in areas of waste ground, rough pastures, road verges and hedgerows where they look for weed seeds. They can also be found occasionally with Siskins, feeding on Alder, Birch and Cupressus.

The population seems to fluctuate as it is affected by severe winters, but breeding success is such that numbers soon become stable again.

Siskin *(Carduelis spinus)*   *Local resident breeding bird and winter visitor*

This small Finch has been recorded in recent years as a sporadic breeding bird, favouring the coniferous woodland of the Northern Pennines and the larch woods of South Lakeland.

The habit of birds visiting bird-tables during the Winter is becoming more frequent in the county. This often occurs in suburban areas and housing estates away from notable woodlands. Siskins seem particularly attracted to the red peanut bags sold to attract Tits and other species to the garden.

Numbers of winter migrants arrive during October, sometimes in large flocks of fifty or more. These flocks roam along river systems looking for Alders and Birches, which is their chief food source.

Linnet *(Acanthis cannabina)*   *Resident breeding bird and winter visitor*

Widespread and locally common in some districts. It is more common on low ground, less numerous in fell areas and is absent in some fell-top localities.

It breeds in gorse and other dense cover on waste ground, commons, rail and road embankments, river banks and occasionally in evergreen cover in gardens.

Winter flocks are often large, particularly near the coast. During this time birds will often mix with other Finches to feed in stubble fields, along the seashore or the tidelines of estuaries. Post-breeding flocks often involve *several hundred* birds and typical is a recorded flock of *c two hundred and twenty-*

five birds on 24 Aug, 1979 at Mallerstang in the east of the county. The unusual feature about this was that the flock went to roost in a large area of bracken (R & D Baines).

Seasonal movements of Linnets often involve birds in a north-south and return passage. Only one Continental ringing return occurred in the period. A bird ringed on 26 Jun, 1966 at Walney Bird Observatory was recovered on 23 Oct, 1966 at Gironde, France.

Twite *(Acanthis flavirostris)*   *Sparse resident breeding bird and winter visitor*

The Twite has never been a common breeding bird in Cumbria. A small population breeds annually in the Pennines, with a few scattered pairs in the Lakeland Fells in the north and the Central and Shap Fells in the south.

It is apparent that the bird has increased in the last twenty years in the south of the county as small family parties were found in the summer months on Sunbiggin Moor (1976), Kentmere (1979), and Wet Sleddale (1983). A nest found in 1976 on Sunbiggin Moor was well documented (Birds in Cumbria, 76/77, p 25) when it was unsuccessfully parasitised by a Cuckoo (R W Robson). A further increase seems imminent as *three* birds were found on Black Coombe and *two* on Kirkby Moor, Ulverston, in May 1984.

Since 1980, post-breeding flocks have been recorded in the Pennines around the Alston/Nenthead area, *c seventy* on 28 Aug, 1980 at Nenthead (B Armstrong) being typical.

In the winter months the local population is increased by immigrants from the north. Flocks of *eighty* to *one hundred and twenty* can be found on the estuaries, saltmarshes and coastal shoreline. The Solway marshes are the most favoured site for these flocks.

Redpoll *(Acanthis flammea)*   *Resident breeding bird and winter visitor*

This is a bird of local distribution favouring open woodland, mature hedgerows and conifer plantations. They are often found up to the tree line in the Pennines and in the Central Fells. Numbers increase in the Autumn and Winter months with flocks containing *fifty* or so birds being commonplace. They are to be found on lake shorelines and river valleys where they favour Alder and Birch seed for food. The Winter of 1983/84 was remarkable for large parties of Redpoll throughout the county, *c two hundred and fifty,* 21 Nov, 1983 at Naddle Forest, Haweswater, being a notable flock.

Ringing returns have come from various sites in the country with a bird ringed on 18 Sep, 1977 at Dubbs Moss, Eaglesfield, found dead on 3 Dec, 1977 at Vicanza, Italy.

The sub-species, Mealy and Arctic Redpoll have not been recorded in the county in the period under review.

Two-barred Crossbill *(Loxia leucoptera)*   *Vagrant*
Stokoe's BLC refers to two old records of birds in north Cumberland during the winter of 1845/46 and a male at Maryport in Sep, 1908.

A recent record of a *female* seen on 10 Aug, 1978 at the southern end of Thirlmere (B Armitage) has not been authenticated by the BBRC at the time of writing.

Crossbill *(Loxia curvirostra)*   *Local resident breeding bird and irruptive migrant*
Periodic irruptions of Crossbills from Northern Europe in late summer, often brings birds to Cumbria. When this occurs they often establish themselves in suitable breeding habitat for a year or so. In the last ten years or so breeding pairs have been recorded in the woodland around Lake Windermere and Thirlmere, as well as in Grizedale Forest in the south and Kershope Forest in the north.

It is a bird of coniferous forest in the main, but has also been seen in the open Larch woodland of the limestone areas in the south of the county.

Parrot Crossbill *(Loxia pytyopsittacus)*   *Vagrant*
Stokoe's BLC quotes two old records of two in 1850 by the River Irthing and three in 1865 at New Cross, both in the north of the county.

Scarlet Rosefinch *(Carpodacus erythrinus)*   *Vagrant*
The first and only record to date was surprisingly a singing male, 31 May-3 Jun. 1984 at Allersteads, near Lanercost (J Miles, M F Carrier). Normally only females and immature males have been seen in Britain of this vagrant, making this record very unusual.

Bullfinch *(Pyrrhula pyrrhula)*   *Resident breeding bird*
The Bullfinch is a common and widespread breeding bird in the county, which is resident throughout the year. It favours areas of waste ground where Hawthorn and Birch predominate, as well as the edges of woodland and gardens with shrubberies.

There is some dispersal during Autumn and Winter when family groups of up to *fifteen* birds can be found wandering countryside hedgerows. Damp sites are often visited at this time, where they feed on the seed of Meadow Sweet, Dock and other weeds.

The Northern race of the Bullfinch is a rare visitor to Cumbria, but a *pair* of this race was found in Dec, 1974 at Murton, Appleby by E Hinchcliffe and a *female* was trapped and ringed on 10 Oct, 1982 at Siddick Pond by J C Callion.

Hawfinch *(Coccothraustes coccothraustes)*   *Irregular breeding resident*

Where the Hawfinch is established in Cumbria, it seems to have increased in numbers in the last twenty years.

It favours open woodland, large gardens and parks where trees like Hornbeam, Wild Cherry and Yew predominate. It is rather a secretive bird which tends to keep to the top of tree cover.

It is found in several areas in the south of the county, particularly throughout the Kent Valley and around Lake Windermere and Coniston Water. Further north it occurs in Borrowdale and around Derwentwater. It remains scarce in Furness in the south-west and in the Eden Valley and along the Solway Plain in the north.

Flocks of *twenty-five* or so birds have been found in some districts between September and March.

White-throated Sparrow *(Zonotrichia albicollis)*   *Vagrant*

A male was trapped and ringed on 18 Jun, 1965 at Walney Bird Observatory (H Tickle, E Pithers *et al*). This was the third record of this American vagrant to be recovered in Britain.

The recovery of this bird at the newly formed Observatory gave the ringing team an encouraging start to their project. The record was accepted by the BBRC.

Lapland Bunting *(Calcarius lapponicus)*   *Scarce winter visitor*

This is an irregular winter visitor which generally occurs along the Cumbrian coast. A very unusual record was of a *male* seen on 5 May, 1959 on the shore of Derwentwater, in Larches with Redpoll and other finches. This bird was identified at close range and sketched by Mrs E J Wilson. Other records in the last twenty-five years include;

>   *Immature female,* 26 Apr, 1968, North Walney (K Brown).
>   *One,* 5 Oct, 1968, Walney Bird Observatory.
>   *Male,* 18 Oct, 1969, Silecroft (R S Wimpress).

Male, 23 Sep & 1 Nov, 1970, Walney Bird Observatory.
Male, 5 May, 1980, Rockcliffe Marsh Nature Reserve
(D & J Bailey, J & L Hiskett).
Immature, 30 Nov-1 Dec, 1982, Walney Bird Observatory.
Immature male, 2-4 Dec, 1983, Walney Bird Observatory.
One, 5 Nov, 1984, Walney Bird Observatory.

Snow Bunting *(Plectrophenax nivalis)*   *Winter visitor and*
passage migrant

This winter visitor occurs in small numbers each year around
the coast from Moricambe Bay to Workington on the Solway
and around Walney Island. Sometimes large numbers seek
refuge on the coast during severe weather conditions.
Examples of this during the period include; *c one hundred*
10 Nov, 1981 at Anthorn; *c three hundred and fifty,* 24-27 Jan,
1984, South Walney and *c one hundred and eighty,* 27 Jan, 1984 at
North Walney.

It is also a regular visitor to the summits of the Lake District
mountains and the Pennines, particularly above an altitude of
1,500 ft. Records in the period include; *c one hundred and twenty,*
9 Dec, 1973 on Murton Pike, Pennines; *c fifty,* 26 Nov, 1977 on
Kidsty Pike and *c forty-five,* 6 Nov, 1983 on Whernside. A mid-
Summer record is very unusual and probably concerns first
year non-breeding birds. Such was *three,* late July, 1979,
Hartrigg, Kentmere *(per* J W Allen).

Yellowhammer *(Emberiza citrinella)*   *Resident breeding bird*

This attractive Bunting has a widespread breeding
distribution throughout the county, though it is less
numerous away from the arable farmland of the coastal strip,
the Solway Plain and the Eden Valley. It breeds up to 1,000 ft.,
and is generally absent on moorland districts.

In winter a movement to lower ground around the coast
and estuaries is noted when groups of *thirty* plus birds can be
found feeding in mixed flocks of Finches and Buntings. These
flocks favour areas around farmyards or in stubble fields.

An interesting record is of a bird ringed on 19 Feb, 1964 at
Ulverston, which was recovered at the same locality on 2 Feb,
1971, making it seven years old (L A Cowcill).

Cirl Bunting *(Emberiza cirlus)*   *Former rare passage migrant*

The Cirl Bunting was first recorded in Cumbria in 1914, after
which odd birds were seen in different areas of the Solway
Plain during Spring and Autumn. Stokoe's BLC quotes it as a
breeding bird in the 1930's at Greystoke and Seascale. The
last breeding record occurred in 1955 on the north-west

outskirts of Carlisle. None have been recorded in the county since that date.

Ortolan Bunting *(Emberiza hortulana)* Vagrant
The only county record is of a bird found dead on 7 Oct, 1963, by the lighthouse, South Walney.

Little Bunting *(Emberiza pusilla)* Vagrant
Two records for Cumbria of this northern Bunting include a bird found with Linnets on the railway embankment at Siddick Pond, Workington, on 11 Nov, 1948 by R Stokoe and a bird observed by A J Mercer on 22 Sep, 1965 at Walney Bird Observatory. Both records have been accepted by the BBRC.

Reed Bunting *(Emberiza schoeniclus)* Resident breeding bird
The Reed Bunting is a common resident which can be found as a breeding bird in lakeside reedbeds, estuarine marshes, along river valleys, upland marshes and bogs and occasionally in young conifer plantations. It has been recorded breeding as high as 1,500 ft. where suitable scrubby bog is available. Where birds have been found in young conifer plantations, the site is often well away from water.

Flocks of *twenty* or so birds can be found in winter at both inland and coastal marshes. In the severest conditions birds will often visit gardens when they can be found feeding around bird-tables.

There is some evidence of migration during Spring and Autumn, but this usually involves small numbers.

Black-headed Bunting *(Emberiza melanocephela)* Vagrant
A male seen during 8 & 9 Jun, 1970 at Camphill, Maryport, was described by Miss M M Milne as being suspiciously tame. The record has not been submitted to BBRC.

Corn Bunting *(Emberiza calandra) Local resident breeding bird*
This is a local bird which is found along the coast from the Solway to the Walney/Foulney area. Along this coastal strip its numbers are stable with a slight increase in the St Bees area recorded in the last five years. Elsewhere in the Eden and Kent valleys, numbers have dropped dramatically during the period under review, with only the odd pairs left in each locality.

In Winter, parties of up to *thirty* birds can be found feeding with Skylarks and other Finches in stubble fields along the coast.

Category D

This is a group of species which have been recorded within the last fifty years and would otherwise appear in the Systematic List except that *(a)* there is reasonable doubt that they have occurred in a wild state, or *(b)* they certainly arrived with ship assistance, or *(c)* they have only ever been found dead on the tideline; also other species which would otherwise appear in the Systematic list except that their feral populations may or may not be self supporting. The main object of Category D is to collect together the records of species which are not yet full additions, so these are not overlooked if there are subsequent fully acceptable records.

Both **Wood Duck** *(Aix sponsa)* and **Barrow's Goldeneye** *(Bucephala islandica)* have been recorded on a few occasions during the period under review on various waters of Cumbria. Both these ducks are listed as Category D but there are so many ornamental wildfowl collections in the county, the probability that they are escapees is high, and so have not been submitted to the BBRC.

Palm Warbler *(Dendroica palmarum)*

A headless corpse was found on the tideline on Walney Island on 18 May, 1976. The record was submitted to the BBRC and accepted in principle under Category D (D Satterthwaite, J Sheldon).

Black-headed Grosbeak *(Pheucticus melanocephaus)*

A female of this species frequented a garden at Fellfoot, Staveley from 5-8 May, 1978 (J W Allen, M Hutcheson *et al*). It was submitted to BBRC and accepted in Category D. The bird is a native of Western United States of America.

Painted Bunting *(Passerina ciris)*

A male was found in a garden in Arnside on 4 Apr, 1974 (J A G Barnes *et al*).

Abbreviations

BBRC — British Birds Rarities Committee.
BOEE — Birds of the Estuaries Enquiry.
BOU — British Ornithological Union.
BTO — British Trust for Ornithology.
CBR — Cumbria Bird Report.
MBWG — Morecambe Bay Wader Group.
RSPB — Royal Society for the Protection of Birds.
WBO — Walney Bird Observatory.
→ — direction of flight.

PRINCIPAL WATERFOWL FIGURES

CANADA GOOSE — maxima at main sites

	1974	75	76	77	78	79	80	81	82	83	84	average
Eden valley (Culgaith area)	200	92	—	68	178	—	87	220	330	270	218	185
Thirlmere	26	—	—	10	—	200	—	188	289	120	—	139
Wyndhammere							168	130	185	112	84	135
Killington Reservoir	100	119	112	114	112	132	119	170	139	118	210	131
Haweswater	12	14	12	25	71	60	112	160	156	102	—	72
Derwentwater	34	40	19	32	59	67	74	38	53	53	41	46
Bassenthwaite Water				14	3	23	5	75	80	—	39	34
Wet Sleddale Dam					4	—	80	—	36	53	28	27

Other sites holding up to an average of 25 birds.
Crummock Water; Loweswater; Ullswater; Grasmere; Rydal and Esthwaite Water.

GREYLAG GOOSE — maxima at main sites (including feral population)

	1974	75	76	77	78	79	80	81	82	83	84	average
Eden Valley	750	2400	1300	2150	2400	2200	1400	2000	1300	2000	2100	1727
Whins Pond							800	600	120	—	—	380
Bassenthwaite Water			237	230	50	357	116	300	610	120	290	257
Aglionby (River Eden)					250	104	70	250	200	—	150	171
Kent Estuary	420	228	150	142	220	155	160	16	16	90	144	158
Muncaster		60	—	100	190	112	—	50	117	87	—	102

Other sites holding under the average of a hundred birds;
Derwentwater; Haweswater; Esthwaite Water; Windermere; Rydal; Coniston Water; Crummock Water and Loweswater

WIGEON — maxima at top ten main sites

	1974	75	76	77	78	79	80	81	82	83	84	average
North Walney	520	—	—	—	—	—	—	950	650	1024	1600	949
South Walney	—	600	1200	750	1000	500	1000	1000	600	500	609	776
Cavendish Dock, Barrow	—	—	1500	400	1100	345	—	—	—	425	500	712
Ravenglass	—	500	995	736	—	110	350	—	350	—	307	478
Foulney Island/Roosecote	535	—	250	—	—	—	552	875	200	400	244	437
Leven Estuary							300	650		195	70	305
Bassenthwaite Water						300	300			205	430	249
Eskmeals Nature Reserve		338	800	150		30	300	110	110	50		228
Longtown Gravel Pits				100	100		120	250				189
Flookburgh Marshes					84				210			126

TEAL — maxima with average over one hundred

	1974	75	76	77	78	79	80	81	82	83	84	average
South Walney			1250	1400		—	1500	1500	900	700	530	1111
Hodbarrow			150	—	629	625	330	600	600	600	700	529
Bassenthwaite Water							140	140	92	—	992	341
Leven Estuary					200	—	500	122	500	280	320	320
Crofthead Gravel Pits (Longtown)							80	120	260	200	—	165
Helton Tarn	165		—	110	184	120	100	120	—	70	—	125

Other sites with average over 50 (* indicates one count only)

*Ravenglass 250; *Barfield Tarn, Bootle 250; *Kitmere 110; Siddick Pond 96; Wet Sleddale Dam 83; Upper Kent Estuary 83; Sunbiggin Tarn 81; Lyth Valley 79; Esthwaite Water 73; Derwentwater 55.

119

MALLARD — maxima at top ten sites

	1978	1979	1980	1981	1982	1983	1984	average
Lake Windermere	1666	1600	2393	1782	1967	2009	1678	1871
Upper Solway			1200	1745	330		207	870
Kent Estuary					450	657	900	657
Bassenthwaite Water	307	903	338	898	317		992	626
Hodbarrow			368	700	430	187	510	439
Longtown Gravel Pits	78	406	400			670		388
Leven Estuary					200	400	500	367
Coniston Water			336	126	332	302	214	262
Wet Sleddale Dam	194	262	262	254	255		270	253
Haweswater	217	249	460	65		272		248

TUFTED DUCK — maxima at top ten sites

	1974	75	76	77	78	79	80	81	82	83	84	average
Lake Windermere	400	—	332	290	472	462	502	412	439	343	642	429
Cavendish Dock				120	270	250	250	390	445	256	375	294
Bassenthwaite Water	150	43	128	173	139	548	867	571	223	77	243	287
Esthwaite Water		83	153	100	198	139	185	123	147		117	138
Hodbarrow				170	177	42	80	154		98	29	107
Siddick Pond	150	60										105
Elterwater		100	—			74	120		85	90	70	79
Grasmere			—					65	75	57	106	76
Derwentwater							87	82	95	54	42	72
Longtown Gravel Pits			27	75	90	94						72

POCHARD — maxima with average over one hundred

	1974	75	76	77	78	79	80	81	82	83	84	average
Cavendish Dock				620	520	320	320	546	284	280	260	393
Lake Windermere			61	62	157	157	301	168	591	206	459	240
Coniston Water				60	—	21	238	238	302	302	169	190
Bassenthwaite Water		27	145	48	69	514	100	223	82	82	8	129
Hodbarrow				230	183	119	34	100		51	—	120
Derwentwater	200	120	—	105	101	113	155	112	112	89	18	113

Other sites over an average of 25.

Whinfell Tarn 61; Longtown Gravel Pits 58; Siddick Pond 43; Esthwaite Water 40; Whins Pond 40; Crummock Water 35; Rydal Water 34; Grasmere 27; Urswick Tarn 27; Fisher Tarn 27; Tarn House Tarn, Kirkby Stephen 26.

GOLDENEYE — maxima with an average over 50

	1974	75	76	77	78	79	80	81	82	83	84	average
Lake Windermere	295	—	188	222	229	284	276	239	—	263	232	248
Rockcliffe Nature Reserve	—		360	100	200	20	150	150	100	62	80	136
Bassenthwaite Water			117	117	37	55	105	57	95	95	98	86
Leven Estuary				50	56	70	48	81	75	73	84	67
Hodbarrow		62	58	62	24	100	30	52	28	127	—	60
Carlisle (River Eden)		70	115	60	14	6	90	—	10	—	—	52

Other sites over an average of 10.

Cavendish Dock 44; South Walney 37; Esthwaite Water 30; Upper Kent Estuary 30; Siddick Pond 29; Ravenglass 22; Longtown Gravel Pits 18; Derwentwater 17; Killington Reservoir 13; Haweswater 12; Over Water 12.

RED BREASTED MERGANSER — maxima with an average over 50

	1974	75	76	77	78	79	80	81	82	83	84	average
Hodbarrow	—	—	24	170	184	290	292	250	—	250	62	190
Cavendish Dock	—	33	109	—	120	250	70	—	194	115	125	116
Kirksanton/Silecroft			76			18	26		180		62	72
Lake Windermere	28	37				—					96	53

Other sites over an average of 20.

Foulney Island 42; Derwentwater 39; Ravenglass 38; Leven Estuary 30; Kent Estuary 27; Rockcliffe Nature Reserve 20.

GOOSANDER — maxima with an average over 20

	1974	75	76	77	78	79	80	81	82	83	84	average
Longtown Gravel Pits									35	—	52	44
Talkin Tarn			45	—	24	34	29	18	30	37	28	37
Rockcliffe Nature Reserve				50	24	32	40	12	50	32	24	33
Kitmere					24	—	39	44	15	9	7	23
Killington Reservoir	10		9	59	12	—	52	—	8	10	17	22
Derwentwater			33	30	—	—	22	11	11	16	24	21

Other sites over an average of 10.

Wet Sleddale Dam 20; Wyndhammere 20; Ennerdale 18; Carlisle (River Eden) 18; Ennerdale 18; Grasmere 17; Elterwater 17; Warcop (River Eden) 17; Haweswater 17; Upper Kent Estuary 15; Ullswater 14; Mosedale Tarn 14; Bassenthwaite Water 13; Grayrigg Tarn 13; Culgaith (River Eden) 12; Borwick Fold Tarn 12.

	1974	75	76	77	78	79	80	81	82	83	84	average
COOT — maxima at main sites												
Lake Windermere	915	—	972	1054	1240	922	1215	1260	929	1145	1182	1083
Bassenthwaite Water	200	160	390	600	1102	200	602	634	450	—	423	476
Derwentwater		370	—	670	441	670	583	690	477	254	36	466
Cavendish Dock			152	250	400	400	410	515	625	600	553	434
Hodbarrow			384	—	508	452	128	600	270	130	215	336
Ullswater			244	61	728	184	154	417	161	—	—	278
Longtown Gravel Pits					240	270	192	—	—	—	332	259
Thurstonfield Lough					205	170	232	—	—	—	225	208
Talkin Tarn				190	—	202	—	180	—	—	—	190
Esthwaite Water	142	103	98	—	123	112	—	—	—	—	120	116
Sunbiggin Tarn			86	107	93	117	115	130	26	20	105	89

1985 RECORDS

A list of the more unusual sightings throughout the county.

Black-throated Diver
Inland records include:— *One,* 20 Jan, Ullswater (D Thomason); *One,* 20 Jan, Thirlmere (Miss K M Atkinson); *One,* 14 Jan-21 Feb and 16-22 Dec, Coniston Water.

Great Northern Diver
Inland records include:— *Two,* 20 Jan, Thirlmere (Miss K M Atkinson); *One,* 5 Jan-25 Feb, Coniston Water.

Slavonian Grebe
One, 3-12 Mar, R Eden, Rockcliffe (A Cremin). The only inland record.

Black-necked Grebe
One, 15 Nov, River Lowther, Helton (P & D Shirley). The only inland record.

Cory's Shearwater
One, 12 Jun, North Walney (J & J Sheldon); *Singles,* 13 Jun, 20 Aug & 16 Sep, Walney Bird Observatory

Great Shearwater
One, 2 Aug, North Walney (J & J Sheldon).

Leach's Petrel
One, 14 Sep, *Six,* 16 Sep, *Two,* 21 Sep, Walney Bird Observatory.

Bittern
One, 20 Feb, Bassenthwaite Lake Marsh (D Thomason).

Black Stork
Immature, 10 Sep, Milburn, Eden Valley (A Elliott). The bird moved on to Abbeytown in the Solway Plain (J J Carruthers). The bird was then found on 18 Sep at Melbourne Park, Carlisle (G Horne) where it remained for a few days, obviously getting weaker in health. It was taken into care by the RSPCA for a month, before being released on 25 Oct at Hallbankgate, Brampton. Amazingly, it was found later the same day at Walney Bird Observatory (T Dean) in company with a *second* bird, this time an adult. The adult moved on, but the immature stayed on Walney until 1 Nov. This is the first record of Black Stork in Cumbria.

Spoonbill
Two, 26-31 Aug, Sandgate Marsh, Flookburgh (F Tinker).

Ruddy Duck
Male, 9 Aug, River Eden, Abbot Moss, Armathwaite (M F Carrier).

Male, 27-30 Apr, Mockerkin Tarn (D Holloway).

Male, 2 Feb-21 Apr, Bassenthwaite Lake (D Thomason, J C Callion *et al*).

Female, 20-27 Sep, Siddick Pond, Workington (J C Callion, N White).

Male, 19 Jan-23 Feb; *Pair,* 15-17 Feb, Cavendish Dock, Barrow (D Satterthwaite, A J Mackenzie *et al*).

Honey Buzzard
One, 15 Aug, Rusland Heights (H Stables), moving southwards.

One, 1 Sep, Walney Bird Observatory (T Dean).

These are the first records of this bird in the county since 1925.

Red Kite
One, 17 Mar, Cummersdale, Carlisle (B Marrs).

One, 17 Jul, Kirkby Lonsdale (F Johnston).

Marsh Harrier
Female, 29 May, Walney Bird Observatory (T Dean), with another different female being seen 31 May, North Walney (J & J Sheldon).

Rough-legged Buzzard
One, 22 Oct, Tindale (J Miles) — moving westwards; *One,* 17 Mar, Shap Fell (D G Newell); *One,* 3 Nov, Burnbanks, Haweswater (D G Walker) — moving westwards.

Hobby
Immature, 12 Sep, Newton Arlosh, Solway (D Irving); *One,* 4 Jul, Middleton Common, Lune Valley (J V Bhalerao); *One,* 12-27 Oct, Walney Island (T Dean, J & J Sheldon).

Quail
Male calling, 20 Jun, Walney airfield (P Anderson).

Spotted Crake
One, 21 Jul, Walney Bird Observatory (T Dean).

Stone Curlew
One, 28 Sep, Walney Bird Observatory (D Satterthwaite, T Dean).

Little Stint
One, over-wintering, seen 20 Jan, Sandside, Kent Estuary (A F Gould).

Pomarine Skua
Several seen around Walney Island during the Autumn, but *seven,* 14 Sep on the Inner Solway (B Marrs, J Hamer, J Miles) during a westerly gale is noteworthy.

Long-tailed Skua
Singles on 26 May and 13 Jun off Walney Island (M Cope, S Hughes, T Dean) were the first sightings of this rare Skua for nineteen years.

Mediterranean Gull
Adult, 20 Jan, Foulney Island (C Johnson).

Iceland Gull
Second year birds were seen on 4 Feb, at Keswick tip (D Satterthwaite); on 14 Apr, Walney Bird Observatory (T Dean); 23 Apr, Siddick Pond, Workington (J C Callion) and 24 Jul, at Milton tip, Brampton (J Miles).

White-winged Black Tern
A record of a bird seen on 29 May, Rockcliffe Marsh, Solway (K Hindmarch) is at the time of publication being validated by British Birds Rarities Committee.

Wryneck
One, 6 Sep, White Moss, Carlisle airport (R Jerram).

Richard's Pipit
One, 3 Sep, Walney Bird Observatory (T Dean).

Water Pipit
One, 22 Mar, Rooscote Bay, Barrow (D Satterthwaite).

Bluethroat
A bird of the white-spotted race found on 10 May, Loweswater (A A Armstrong) is additional to the two red-spotted birds referred to in the Systematic List and makes the total of five records in Cumbria.

Melodious Warbler
One, 11 Sep, Walney Bird Observatory (T Dean).

Yellow-browed Warbler
One, 26 Sep, and *two,* 18 Oct, Walney Bird Observatory (T Dean).

Red-breasted Flycatcher
Three, 26 Sep, Walney Bird Observatory (T Dean) — these birds along with the Yellow-browed Warbler were part of a very unusual 'fall' in the Morecambe Bay area.

Red-backed Shrike
Male, 16 May, North Walney (S Lawson, T Dean).

REFERENCES

Association of Natural History Societies in Cumbria, 1970-74, *Natural History in Cumbria.*

Association of Natural History Societies in Cumbria, 1975-85, *Birds in Cumbria.* Annual County Natural History Reports.

'British Birds' Rarities Committee, Annual report on Rare Birds in Britain.

Brown, R. H., 1974, *Lakeland Birdlife* 1920-1970. Thurnam, Carlisle.

Cramp, S. & Simmons, K. E. L., 1977, *The Birds of the Western Palearctic,* Vol. 1; 1980, Vol. 2; 1983, Vol 3; 1985, Vol 4. Oxford.

Evans, A. C., 1971, *The Naturalist's Lake District.* Dalesman, Clapham.

Grant, P. J., 1982, *Gulls. A Guide to Identification.* Poyser.

Hardy, E., 1979, *Birdwatching in Lancashire.* Dalesman.

Hollom, P. A. D., 1952, *The Popular Handbook of British Birds.* Witherby.

Hollom, P. A. D., 1980, *The Popular Handbook of Rarer British Birds.* Witherby.

Hudson, R., 1973, *Early and Late Dates for Summer Migrants.* B.T.O. Guide No. 15.

Lancashire and Cheshire Fauna Society, *Lancashire Bird Reports.* Annual Reports.

Lancaster and District Birdwatching Society, Annual Bird Reports.

Macpherson, H. A., 1892, *A Vertebrate Fauna of Lakeland.* Edinburgh.

Marsh, P. J. and R., 1979, *Birds of Lancaster and District, 1968-79.* L.D.B.W.S. check-list.

Mitchell, W. R. and Robson, R. W., 1974, *Lakeland Birds.* Dalesman.

Mitchell, W. R. and Robson, R. W., 1973, *Pennine Birds.* Dalesman.

Morecambe Bay Wader Group, Annual Reports.

Peterson, R., Mountford, G. and Hollom, P. A. D., 1954, *A Field Guide to the Birds of Britain and Ireland.* Collins.

Prater, A. J., 1981, *Estuary Birds of Britain and Ireland.* Poyser.

Ruxton, J., 1974, *Wildfowl of Morecambe Bay.* W.A.G.B.I. booklet.

Sharrock, J. T. R., 1976, *The Atlas of Breeding Birds in Britain and Ireland.* Poyser.

Sharrock, J. T. R., 1980, *The Frontiers of Bird Identification (British Birds).* Macmillan.

Sharrock, J. T. R., 1974, *Scarce Migrant Birds in Britain and Ireland.* Poyser.

Sharrock, J. T. R. and E. M., 1976, *Rare Birds in Britain and Ireland.* Poyser.

Snow, D. W., 1971, *The Status of Birds in Britain and Ireland* (B.O.U.). Blackwell.

Spencer, K. G., 1973, *The Status and Distribution of Birds in Lancashire.* Turner & Earnshaw, Bolton.

Stokoe, R., 1964, *The Birds of the Lake Counties.* Thurnam.

Walney Bird Observatory, Annual Reports, 1964-71 and 1980-84.

Wilson, J., 1974, *The Birds of Morecambe Bay.* Dalesman.

PERSONAL CHECK-LIST

	Location	*Date*
Red-throated Diver	....	....
Black-throated Diver	....	....
Great Northern Diver	....	....
Pied-billed Grebe	....	....
Little Grebe	....	....
Great-crested Grebe	....	....
Red-necked Grebe	....	....
Slavonian Grebe	....	....
Black-necked Grebe	....	....
Fulmar	....	....
Cory's Shearwater	....	....
Great Shearwater	....	....
Sooty Shearwater	....	....
Manx Shearwater	....	....
Wilson's Petrel	....	....
Storm Petrel	....	....
Leach's Petrel	....	....
Gannet	....	....
Cormorant	....	....
Shag	....	....
Bittern	....	....
Little Bittern	....	....
Night Heron	....	....
Squacco Heron	....	....
Cattle Egret	....	....
Little Egret	....	....
Grey Heron	....	....

Purple Heron	....	....
Black Stork	....	....
White Stork	....	....
Glossy Ibis	....	....
Spoonbill	....	....
Mute Swan	....	....
Bewick's Swan	....	....
Whooper Swan	....	....
Bean Goose	....	....
Pink-footed Goose	....	....
White-fronted Goose	....	....
Grey-lag Goose	....	....
Snow Goose	....	....
Canada Goose	....	....
Barnacle Goose	....	....
Brent Goose	....	....
Ruddy Shelduck	....	....
Shelduck	....	....
Wigeon	....	....
Gadwall	....	....
Teal	....	....
Mallard	....	....
Pintail	....	....
Garganey	....	....
Shoveler	....	....
Red-crested Pochard	....	....
Pochard	....	....
Ring-necked Duck	....	....
Ferruginous Duck	....	....

Tufted Duck	....	....
Scaup	....	....
Eider	....	....
King Eider	....	....
Long-tailed Duck	....	....
Common Scoter	....	....
Surf Scoter	....	....
Velvet Scoter	....	....
Goldeneye	....	....
Smew	....	....
Red-breasted Merganser	....	....
Goosander	....	....
Ruddy Duck	....	....
Honey Buzzard	....	....
Red Kite	....	....
White-tailed Eagle	....	....
Marsh Harrier	....	....
Hen Harrier	....	....
Montagu's Harrier	....	....
Goshawk	....	....
Sparrow Hawk	....	....
Buzzard	....	....
Rough-legged Buzzard	....	....
Golden Eagle	....	....
Osprey	....	....
Kestrel	....	....
Red-footed Falcon	....	....
Merlin	....	....
Hobby	....	....

Gyrfalcon ....

Peregrine ....

Red Grouse ....

Ptarmigan ....

Black Grouse ....

Capercaillie ....

Red-legged Partridge ....

Grey Partridge ....

Quail ....

Pheasant ....

Water Rail ....

Spotted Crake ....

Little Crake ....

Baillon's Crake ....

Corncrake ....

Moorhen ....

Coot ....

Crane ....

Demoiselle Crane ....

Great Bustard ....

Oystercatcher ....

Avocet ....

Stone Curlew ....

Cream-coloured Courser ....

Collared Pratincole ....

Little Ringed Plover ....

Ringed Plover ....

Dotterel ....

Golden Plover ....

Grey Plover ....

Knot ....

Sanderling ....

Little Stint ....

Temminck's Stint ....

White-rumped Sandpiper ....

Baird's Sandpiper ....

Pectoral Sandpiper ....

Curlew Sandpiper ....

Purple Sandpiper ....

Dunlin ....

Buff-breasted Sandpiper ....

Ruff ....

Jack Snipe ....

Snipe ....

Great Snipe ....

Dowitcher ....

Woodcock ....

Black-tailed Godwit ....

Bar-tailed Godwit ....

Whimbrel ....

Curlew ....

Spotted Redshank ....

Redshank ....

Greenshank ....

Lesser Yellowlegs ....

Green Sandpiper ....

Wood Sandpiper ....

Common Sandpiper ....

Turnstone	....	....
Red-necked Phalarope	....	....
Grey Phalarope	....	....
Pomarine Skua	....	....
Arctic Skua	....	....
Long-tailed Skua	....	....
Great Skua	....	....
Mediterranean Gull	....	....
Laughing Gull	....	....
Little Gull	....	....
Sabine's Gull	....	....
Black-headed Gull	....	....
Ring-billed Gull	....	....
Common Gull	....	....
Lesser Black-backed Gull	....	....
Herring Gull	....	....
Iceland Gull	....	....
Glaucous Gull	....	....
Great Black-backed Gull	....	....
Kittiwake	....	....
Ivory Gull	....	....
Sandwich Tern	....	....
Roseate Tern	....	....
Common Tern	....	....
Arctic Tern	....	....
Sooty Tern	....	....
Little Tern	....	....
Whiskered Tern	....	....
Black Tern	....	....

White-winged Black Tern	....	....
Guillemot	....	....
Razorbill	....	....
Black Guillemot	....	....
Little Auk	....	....
Puffin	....	....
Pallas's Sandgrouse	....	....
Rock Dove	....	....
Stock Dove	....	....
Woodpigeon	....	....
Collared Dove	....	....
Turtle Dove	....	....
Cuckoo	....	....
Barn Owl	....	....
Scop's Owl	....	....
Snowy Owl	....	....
Little Owl	....	....
Tawny Owl	....	....
Long-eared Owl	....	....
Short-eared Owl	....	....
Tengmalm's Owl	....	....
Nightjar	....	....
Swift	....	....
Alpine Swift	....	....
Kingfisher	....	....
Bee-eater	....	....
Roller	....	....
Hoopoe	....	....
Wryneck	....	....

Green Woodpecker	....	....
Great Spotted Woodpecker	....	....
Lesser Spotted Woodpecker	....	....
Woodlark	....	....
Skylark	....	....
Shore Lark	....	....
Sand Martin	....	....
Swallow	....	....
House Martin	....	....
Richard's Pipit	....	....
Tawny Pipit	....	....
Tree Pipit	....	....
Meadow Pipit	....	....
Rock Pipit	....	....
Water Pipit	....	....
Yellow Wagtail	....	....
Grey Wagtail	....	....
Pied Wagtail	....	....
White Wagtail	....	....
Waxwing	....	....
Dipper	....	....
Wren	....	....
Dunnock	....	....
Robin	....	....
Nightingale	....	....
Bluethroat	....	....
Black Redstart	....	....
Redstart	....	....

Whinchat ....

Stonechat ....

Isabelline Wheatear ....

Wheatear ....

Ring Ousel ....

Blackbird ....

Fieldfare ....

Song Thrush ....

Redwing ....

Mistle Thrush ....

American Robin ....

Grasshopper Warbler ....

Savi's Warbler ....

Sedge Warbler ....

Paddyfield Warbler ....

Reed Warbler ....

Icterine Warbler ....

Melodious Warbler ....

Barred Warbler ....

Lesser Whitethroat ....

Whitethroat ....

Garden Warbler ....

Blackcap ....

Pallas's Warbler ....

Yellow-browed Warbler ....

Bonelli's Warbler ....

Wood Warbler ....

Chiffchaff ....

Willow Warbler ....

Goldcrest	....	....
Firecrest	....	....
Spotted Flycatcher	....	....
Red-breasted Flycatcher	....	....
Pied Flycatcher	....	....
Bearded Tit	....	....
Long-tailed Tit	....	....
Marsh Tit	....	....
Willow Tit	....	....
Crested Tit	....	....
Coal Tit.	....	....
Blue Tit	....	....
Great Tit	....	....
Nuthatch	....	....
Treecreeper	....	....
Golden Oriole	....	....
Red-backed Shrike	....	....
Great Grey Shrike	....	....
Woodchat Shrike	....	....
Jay	....	....
Magpie	....	....
Nutcracker	....	....
Chough	....	....
Jackdaw	....	....
Rook	....	....
Carrion Crow	....	....
Hooded Crow	....	....
Raven	....	....

Starling ....

Rose-coloured Starling ....

House Sparrow ....

Tree Sparrow ....

Chaffinch ....

Brambling ....

Greenfinch ....

Goldfinch ....

Siskin ....

Linnet ....

Twite ....

Redpoll ....

Two-barred Crossbill ....

Crossbill ....

Parrot Crossbill ....

Scarlet Rosefinch ....

Bullfinch ....

Hawfinch ....

White-throated Sparrow ....

Lapland Bunting ....

Snow Bunting ....

Yellowhammer ....

Cirl Bunting ....

Ortolan Bunting ....

Little Bunting ....

Reed Bunting ....

Black-headed Bunting ....

Corn Bunting ....